# SOLVABLE CASES OF THE DECISION PROBLEM

# STUDIES IN LOGIC

AND

# THE FOUNDATIONS OF MATHEMATICS


L. E. J. BROUWER
E. W. BETH
A. HEYTING

*Editors*



1962

NORTH-HOLLAND PUBLISHING COMPANY
AMSTERDAM

# SOLVABLE CASES OF THE DECISION PROBLEM

BY

W. ACKERMANN

*Hon. Professor of Mathematical Logic and Foundations of Mathematics University of Münster*

1962

NORTH-HOLLAND PUBLISHING COMPANY
AMSTERDAM

*1st printing 1954*
*2nd printing 1962*



PRINTED IN THE NETHERLANDS

CONTENTS

# PREFACE

This book is intended to give a survey of the more important cases of the decision problem for the predicate calculus with equality of the first and second order which have so far been solved. It strictly restricts to this subject. Other investigations connected with the said problem, e.g. the reduction theorems, are only mentioned as far as they are of relevance for the selection of special cases.

There was the alternative to give a syntactic or a semantic formulation of the decision problem. The author has chosen the second way, though this implies the use of set-theoretic concepts. For a syntactic formulation would have to be preceded by the proof of completeness for a certain system of axioms, which can only be done by semantic methods. Furthermore, a semantic formulation is more convenient if the class of special cases is not restricted to formulas of the first order calculus and if we consider not only the problem of universal validity, but also the problem of determining the domains for which a given formula is valid or not valid. To regard both formulations of the problem would have gone beyond the limits of the book. Relations to systems of axioms are therefore not given here in general, but such relations may easily be established.

The report on the more important solutions, e.g. those for the monadic predicate calculus and complete solutions for classes of prefixes, is given in full detail, whereas other rather special solutions are only mentioned.

The author has been trying to give a systematic treatment as far as this is possible regarding the nature of the subject so that the different methods which have proved successful, are elaborated. For instance, the reduction to the monadic predicate calculus has been used wherever it was possible. No effort has been taken to exhibit such decision methods as lead to the desired aim in the smallest number of steps, since the interest in the solution of special cases is chiefly a theoretical one.

The expert reader will recognize how far the treatment of the problems is new (e.g. the methods of chapter III, some of the results of chapter V and VII etc.). Most of the results hitherto known have been extended to the predicate calculus with equality. In chapter VIII there is given a new formulation of the decision problem in a functional calculus instead of in a predicate calculus, which may offer a greater variety for the selection of special problems to be investigated.

The compilation of the special cases solved has been made from a general point of symbolic logic. There are certain elementary parts of mathematics, such as elementary algebra, for which solutions of the relative decision problem have been given. These solutions, though important on their part, are only mentioned (cp. page 55), since a report on them would have required a separate treatment.

The book is rather self-contained. The reader is supposed only to possess some general knowledge of the propositional and the predicate calculus, as may be acquired by the lecture of any introduction to mathematical logic.

The author is indebted to Prof. Arnold Schmidt for reading the proofs.

The publishers provided for a linguistic revision of the English text according to the author's wish.

*March 1954* W. ACKERMANN

# I

# VALIDITY AND SATISFIABILITY IN FINITE DOMAINS

## 1. Well-formed formulas

In this book we have to do with a certain formal language. We first give a survey of the *primitive symbols* used in constructing the formulas of this language.

The first group of symbols consists of the *logical constants*. They are "&" (and), "v" (or), "—" (not), "=" (is equal to). "&", "v", "—", "=" are called respectively the *sign of conjunction*, the *sign of disjunction*, the *sign of negation* or the *negation-bar*, and the *sign of equality*. The words set in parentheses may be used in reading the symbols and may also serve to suggest the interpretation in a preliminary way.

A second group of primitive symbols are the *variables*. These are Latin capitals or minuscules to which subscripts or superscripts may be added. We distinguish 1) *propositional variables* (Latin capitals): $X, Y, Z, X_1, X_2, \ldots$; 2) *individual variables* (Latin minuscules, but only those succeeding $r$ in the alphabetic order); $x, y, z, u, v, w, x_1, x_2, \ldots$; 3) *predicate variables* (Latin capitals with superscripts): $G^1, H^1, K^2, G^3, G^4_1, G^5_2, \ldots$. Variables $G^n, H^n, H^n_m, \ldots$ are called *n-adic predicate variables*, the superscript indicating the $n$-adic character. Particularly, $G^1, H^1, \ldots$ are *monadic* predicate variables, $G^2, H^2, \ldots$ *dyadic* ones, and so forth.

A third group of symbols is that of the *quantifiers*. These are in a certain way already complex symbols. They consist of a variable or of a variable preceded by the sign $E$ put into brackets. $(Ex)$, $(EG^1)$, $(EX)$, ... are called *existential* quantifiers; $(x)$, $(G^1)$, $(X)$, ... are *universal quantifiers*. $(Ex)$, $(EG^1)$, ... may be read respectively as "there is an $x$", and "there is a $G^1$, ..."; $(x)$, $(G^1)$ are read respectively as "for all $x$", and "for all $G^1$, ...".

Certain finite sequences of these primitive symbols which we are going to define subsequently, are called *well-formed formulas*.

Later on, we shall introduce other symbols, namely German (Gothic) letters, Greek letters and Latin minuscules preceding *r* in the alphabetic order. These symbols do not augment the list of primitive symbols and do not occur in the well-formed formulas, but are only used in statements about these formulas. In principle we could do without them, but they are very useful in avoiding cumbrous textual explanations.

We now proceed to the notion of *well-formed formula* (abbreviated wff). By this term we understand those, and only those, combinations of symbols which may be shown to be such by a finite number of applications of the following rules *W*1—*W*6.

*W*1. A propositional variable is a wff; the variable is said to occur in a *free* form in the wff.

*W*2. A wff is obtained by placing any $n$ individual variables behind an $n$-adic predicate variable; all the variables are said to occur in a *free* form in the wff. (Examples: $G^2xy$, $G^2xx$, $H^3xyz$.)

*W*3. A wff is obtained by placing an individual variable before and behind the sign of equality; the variables are said to occur in a *free* form in the formula. (Examples: $x=x$, $y=z$.)

*W*4. If $\mathfrak{A}$ is a wff in which there occurs a certain variable in one or more places, but always in a *free* form, another wff is obtained by placing the existential or the universal quantifier for this variable before $\mathfrak{A}$, after $\mathfrak{A}$ has been enclosed by brackets. The occurrence of the variable is said to be *bound* in the new formula. $\mathfrak{A}$ is called the *scope* of the quantifier. The occurrences of the other variables are free or bound, according as they are free or bound in $\mathfrak{A}$. The brackets may be omitted, if $\mathfrak{A}$ does not contain "&" and "v", or if $\mathfrak{A}$ begins with a quantifier the scope of which extends to the end of the formula. (Examples: $(x)x=y$, $(G)Gxx$.)

*W*5. If $\mathfrak{A}$ stands for a wff, $\overline{\mathfrak{A}}$ is a wff; the occurrences of the variables in $\overline{\mathfrak{A}}$ are free or bound, according as they are free or bound in $\mathfrak{A}$.

*W*6. If $\mathfrak{A}$ and $\mathfrak{B}$ stand for wffs and if the same variable does not occur bound in one of them and free in the other, then $(\mathfrak{A})$ & $(\mathfrak{B})$ and $(\mathfrak{A}) \vee (\mathfrak{B})$ are wffs. The brackets may be omitted under the same conditions as in *W*4. The occurrences of the variables are free or bound according as they are free or bound in $\mathfrak{A}$ or $\mathfrak{B}$. (Examples: $F^1x \vee G^2xz$, $X \ \& \ (x)(x=y \vee x=z)$.)

Wffs described by $W1-W3$ are called *prime formulas*. They are wffs that contain no quantifiers and no logical constants except "=".

In the text dealing with wffs we are using another kind of variables called *syntactical variables*. They are designated by *German* (Gothic) letters. $\mathfrak{A}$, $\mathfrak{B}$, $\mathfrak{C}$, $\mathfrak{A}_1$, ... stand for any wffs; they have been used already in formulating the preceding six rules. $\mathfrak{A}(x)$, $\mathfrak{B}(x, G^1)$, ... stand for wffs in which $x$ ($x$ and $G^1$) occur in a free form. $\mathfrak{a}$, $\mathfrak{b}$, $\mathfrak{c}$, ... stand for any individual variable, $\mathfrak{U}$, $\mathfrak{V}$, $\mathfrak{W}$, ... for any propositional variable and $\mathfrak{U}^n$, $\mathfrak{V}^n$, $\mathfrak{W}^n$, ... for any $n$-adic predicate variable. The use of the syntactical variables permits us to express general statements about wffs, or individual variables, or propositional variables, or predicate variables in a short form.

In writing wffs we usually omit the superscript of an $\mathfrak{U}^n$, provided this can be done without danger of misunderstanding. This is generally the case if the same letter with two different superscripts does not occur in the formula.

A wff of the form $(\mathfrak{A}) \ \& \ (\mathfrak{B})$ is called a *conjunction*; $\mathfrak{A}$ and $\mathfrak{B}$ are called the *terms* of the conjunction. $(\mathfrak{A}) \vee (\mathfrak{B})$ is called a *disjunction*, $\mathfrak{A}$ and $\mathfrak{B}$ being the *terms* of the disjunction. A wff $\overline{\mathfrak{A}}$ is called the *negation* of $\mathfrak{A}$.

To reduce further the number of brackets, the following conventions are adopted. If we write $\mathfrak{A}_1 \vee \mathfrak{A}_2 \vee \ldots \vee \mathfrak{A}_n$ or $\mathfrak{A}_1 \ \& \ \mathfrak{A}_2 \ \& \ldots \& \ \mathfrak{A}_n$, this is to mean association to the left. Thus, $\mathfrak{A} \vee \mathfrak{B} \vee \mathfrak{C}$ stands for $(\mathfrak{A} \vee \mathfrak{B}) \vee \mathfrak{C}$, $\mathfrak{A} \ \& \ \mathfrak{B} \ \& \ \mathfrak{C} \ \& \ \mathfrak{D}$ for $((\mathfrak{A} \ \& \ \mathfrak{B}) \ \& \ \mathfrak{C}) \ \& \ \mathfrak{D}$. A wff $\mathfrak{A}_1 \ \& \ldots \& \ \mathfrak{A}_n$, $(\mathfrak{A}_1 \vee \ldots \vee \mathfrak{A}_n)$ is also called a conjunction (a disjunction); $\mathfrak{A}_1, \ldots, \mathfrak{A}_n$ are the conjunction terms (the disjunction terms). The symbol "&" shall have precedence over "v", so that for instance $\mathfrak{A} \ \& \ \mathfrak{B} \vee \mathfrak{C}$ is to be understood as $\mathfrak{A} \ \& \ (\mathfrak{B} \vee \mathfrak{C})$. Sometimes we use the symbols $\rightarrow$ and $\leftrightarrow$ in formulas $\mathfrak{A} \rightarrow \mathfrak{B}$ and $\mathfrak{A} \leftrightarrow \mathfrak{B}$. These are only abbreviations for $\overline{\mathfrak{A}} \vee \mathfrak{B}$ and for $\overline{\mathfrak{A}} \vee \mathfrak{B} \ \& \ \mathfrak{A} \vee \overline{\mathfrak{B}}$.

The wffs described here are those of the so-called *predicate calculus of second order or of second level.*

A wff $\mathfrak{A}$ is called a *P-constituent* of the wff $\mathfrak{B}$ (using an expression of A. Church [3]), if $\mathfrak{A}$ is a part of $\mathfrak{B}$ and $\mathfrak{A}$ is not within the scope of any quantifier in $\mathfrak{B}$, and further, $\mathfrak{A}$ has none of the forms $\overline{\mathfrak{C}}$, $\mathfrak{C}$ & $\mathfrak{D}$ or $\mathfrak{C} \vee \mathfrak{D}$. Every $P$-constituent of a wff is either a prime formula or is a formula beginning with a quantifier and consisting of the quantifier together with its scope.

Example: The $P$-constituents of the wff

$X \vee \overline{(x)(x=y \vee z=u)}$ & $(G)(x)Gx \vee u=v$ are $X$, $(x)(x=y \vee z=u)$, $(G)(x)Gx$, and $u=v$.

## 2. Valuation of well-formed formulas in a finite domain. Validity and satisfiability

The problem with which we are concerned in this book, to state it generally, is how to decide for a given wff whether the assertion it expresses is true. This would require an interpretation of the wff, i.e. a definition of what is meant by its truth in accordance with the adopted meaning of the symbols. But the truth of a wff may depend on extralogical facts. Consider e.g. $(Ex)(Ey)(\overline{x=y})$ which says that there are individuals $x$ and $y$ which are distinct. The wff expresses truth if there are two distinct individuals, and falsity if there are not. Thus we cannot give a definition of the truth of a wff without referring to the supposed number of individuals.

In the following, we first give a truth-definition of the wffs if the number of individuals is finite.

Let $D$ be a domain or set with *k individuals* or elements. Elements of a domain will be designated by Latin minuscules (but only those preceding $r$ in the alphabetic order, since the other letters are reserved for individual variables) with or without subscripts. The elements of $D$ may be $a_1, \ldots, a_k$. By a *monadic propositional function over D* we understand a function which has one of the values $T$ or $F$ for every $a_i$ of $D$. $T$ and $F$ are undefined terms; the choice of the letters suggests "true" and "false". *An n-adic propositional function over D* $(n>1)$ has one of the values $T$ or $F$ for every $n$-tuple $(b_1, \ldots, b_n)$ of elements of $D$. There are only a finite number of propositional functions of every kind, namely $2^{(k^n)}$ $n$-adic propositional functions. Propositional functions over $D$ will be designated by *Greek capitals*. We speak of a *complete assignment* for the free variables of a wff in a domain $D$, if an $n$-adic propositional function over $D$ is assigned to every free $n$-adic predicate variable, an element of $D$ to every free individual variable, and $T$ or $F$ to every free propositional variable occurring in the wff. A complete assignment for a wff without free variables is a vacuous one; complete assignments for a wff will be designated by $\Omega, \Omega_1, \Omega_2, \ldots$. Sometimes assignments for a part of the free variables are also designated by $\Omega, \ldots$.

By the following method of truth-definition we intend to give to each wff $\mathfrak{A}$ the value $T$ or $F$ relative to a complete assignment for the free variables in a domain $D$. The value of $\mathfrak{A}$ depends upon this assignment for the free variables and upon the domain $D$; that is, upon the number $k$ of the elements of $D$. If there are no free variables in $\mathfrak{A}$, the value of $\mathfrak{A}$ depends only upon $k$. The valuation of $\mathfrak{A}$ is completely determined by the following rules $V1 - V6$, which contain a recursion corresponding to the construction of wffs. The rules give a direct valuation of the prime formulas and reduce the valuation of another wff to the valuation of a finite number of wffs for which the total number of quantifiers and logical constants occurring in them is less than the corresponding number for the given wff.

$V1$. A propositional variable has the value which is assigned to it.

$V2$. A wff $\mathfrak{U}^1\mathfrak{a}$ ($\mathfrak{U}^n\mathfrak{a}_1 \ldots \mathfrak{a}_n$) has the value $T$ or $F$, according as the propositional function assigned to $\mathfrak{U}^1$ ($\mathfrak{U}^n$) has this value for $a$ $((a_1, \ldots, a_n))$, $a$ $(a_1, \ldots, a_n)$ being the elements of $D$ assigned to $\mathfrak{a}$ $(\mathfrak{a}_1, \ldots, \mathfrak{a}_n)$.

$V3$. A wff $\mathfrak{a} = \mathfrak{b}$ has the value $T$ or $F$ depending upon whether the elements of $D$ assigned to $\mathfrak{a}$ and $\mathfrak{b}$ are the same or not.

$V4$. $\overline{\mathfrak{A}}$ has the value $T$ ($F$) by an assignment, if $\mathfrak{A}$ has the value $F$ ($T$) by this assignment.

$V5$. A wff $\mathfrak{A}$ & $\mathfrak{B}$ has the value $T$ by an assignment, if both $\mathfrak{A}$ and $\mathfrak{B}$ have the value $T$ for this assignment (dropping the assignment for variables not occurring in $\mathfrak{A}$ resp. $\mathfrak{B}$); a wff $\mathfrak{A} \vee \mathfrak{B}$ has the value $T$ by an assignment, if at least one of the formulas $\mathfrak{A}$ and $\mathfrak{B}$

has the value $T$ for this assignment. In all other cases $\mathfrak{A}$ & $\mathfrak{B}$ and $\mathfrak{A} \vee \mathfrak{B}$ have the value $F$ by the given assignment.

*V*6. A wff $(\mathfrak{U})\mathfrak{A}(\mathfrak{U})$ has the value $T$ by an assignment for the free variables, if $\mathfrak{A}(\mathfrak{U})$ has the value $T$ by the same assignment for the free variables different from $\mathfrak{U}$ and an arbitrary assignment for the variable $\mathfrak{U}$; a wff $(E\mathfrak{U})\mathfrak{A}(\mathfrak{U})$ has the value $T$ for an assignment, if there is an assignment for $\mathfrak{U}$ which together with the given assignment for the free variables of $(E\mathfrak{U})\mathfrak{A}(\mathfrak{U})$ gives the value $T$ to $\mathfrak{A}(\mathfrak{U})$. In every other case, $(\mathfrak{U})\mathfrak{A}(\mathfrak{U})$ and $(E\mathfrak{U})\mathfrak{A}(\mathfrak{U})$ have the value $F$ by an assignment.

The value of wffs $(\mathfrak{a})\mathfrak{A}(\mathfrak{a})$, $(E\mathfrak{a})\mathfrak{A}(\mathfrak{a})$, $(\mathfrak{U}^n)\mathfrak{A}(\mathfrak{U}^n)$, $(E\mathfrak{U}^n)\mathfrak{A}(\mathfrak{U}^n)$ is determined by reference to $\mathfrak{A}(\mathfrak{a})$ or $\mathfrak{A}(\mathfrak{U}^n)$ in the same way as has been done above for $(\mathfrak{U})\mathfrak{A}(\mathfrak{U})$ or $(E\mathfrak{U})\mathfrak{A}(\mathfrak{U})$ by reference to $\mathfrak{A}(\mathfrak{U})$.

*By these six rules $V1-V6$ the valuation of a wff for an assignment for the free variables relative to a domain D with a given finite number of elements is not only uniquely determined, but may also be effectively carried out.* Note that the effectiveness of the procedure is granted only if the number of elements of $D$ is not only finite but fixed and completely known, for instance, if it is 1 or 7 or 285. For in this case we can give a complete list of the monadic propositional functions, of the dyadic propositional functions over $D$, etc., and of the elements of $D$. If an assignment for the free variables of a wff is given, the valuation for this assignment is reduced by *V*6 to the valuation of a simpler wff for a fixed finite number of assignments. By *V*4 and *V*5 it is reduced to the valuation of one or two simpler wffs for a fixed assignment, while $V1-V3$ give a direct valuation for prime formulas.

As an example we consider the wff

$$(z)(Eu)(Ev)(z=u \vee z=v \ \& \ \overline{u=v}) \ \& \ (G)(\overline{x=y} \vee Gxx \vee \overline{Gyy}).$$

This formula contains the two free variables $x$ and $y$. A valuation of the wff in a certain domain $D$ will depend upon the elements assigned to $x$ and $y$.

We first give the valuation for a domain containing only one element designated by $a$. In this case, only $a$ can be assigned to $x$ and $y$ and generally to any individual variable. $u=v$ has the value $T$, and $\overline{u=v}$ the value $F$ for any assignment for $u$ and $v$ according to $V3$ and $V4$; $z=u \vee z=v \;\&\; \overline{u=v}$ has the value $F$ by any assignment (see $V5$). According to $V6$,

$$(Ev)(z=u \vee z=v \;\&\; \overline{u=v}),\quad (Eu)(Ev)(z=u \vee z=v \;\&\; \overline{u=v})$$

and

$$(z)(Eu)(Ev)(z=u \vee z=v \;\&\; \overline{u=v})$$

have the value $F$ for any assignment; the last wff has simply the value $F$, since no free variables occur. According to $V5$, the whole wff gets the value $F$.

Now let $D$ be composed of two elements $a$ and $b$; $c$ and $d$ are two elements of $D$ assigned to $x$ and $y$. $z=u \vee z=v \;\&\; \overline{u=v}$ gets the value $T$ by an assignment, if the elements of $D$ assigned to $u$ and $v$ are different; for as there are only the elements $a$ and $b$, the element assigned to $z$ is the same as one of the elements assigned to $u$ and $v$. Then $z=u \vee z=v$ gets the value $T$ as does $\overline{u=v}$. $(Ev)(z=u \vee z=v \;\&\; \overline{u=v})$ gets the value $T$ by any assignment, since there is an assignment for $v$ which together with the assignment for $z$ and $u$ gets the value $T$ for $z=u \vee z=v \;\&\; \overline{u=v}$. We need only assign to $v$ the element of $D$ different from that assigned to $u$.

$$(Eu)(Ev)(z=u \vee z=v \;\&\; \overline{u=v}) \text{ and } (z)(Eu)(Ev)(z=u \vee z=v \;\&\; \overline{u=v})$$

get the value $T$ in any case. By $V5$ the value of the whole wff is the same as that of the second term of the conjunction, $(G)(\overline{x=y} \vee Gxx \vee \overline{Gyy})$. $\overline{x=y} \vee Gxx \vee \overline{Gyy}$ gets the value $T$ if $c$ and $d$ are not the same elements, since in this case $\overline{x=y}$ and therefore the whole disjunction gets the value $T$. If $c$ and $d$ are the same elements, $Gxx$ and $Gyy$ get the same value by any assignment of a propositional function to $G$, so that $Gxx \vee \overline{Gyy}$ and $\overline{x=y} \vee Gxx \vee \overline{Gyy}$ get the value $T$. As this is independent on the assignment for $G$, $(G)(\overline{x=y} \vee Gxx \vee \overline{Gyy})$ gets the value $T$ for any assignment for $x$ and $y$. The value of the wff

$$(z)(Eu)(Ev)(z=u \vee z=v \;\&\; \overline{u=v}) \;\&\; (G)(\overline{x=y} \vee Gxx \vee \overline{Gyy})$$

is therefore $T$ in a domain with two elements, no matter which elements of $D$ are assigned to $x$ and $y$.

If the universal quantifiers for $x$ and $y$ are placed before the wff, their scopes extending to the end of the wff, this new wff gets the value $T$ in a domain with two elements. It gets the value $F$ in a domain with one element, as was shown above.

*A wff containing no free variables is called valid in a domain D, if it gets the value T in D.*

It is customary to define the notion of validity also for wffs containing free variables. A wff of this kind is called valid in a domain $D$, if the wff is valid which results from it by placing the universal quantifiers for the free variables in any succession before the wff, the scopes of the quantifiers extending to the end of the wff. A wff containing free variables is said to be *satisfiable* in a domain $D$, if the wff is valid which results from it by placing the existential quantifiers for the free variables in any succession before the wff, their scopes extending to the end of the wff.

With regard to the last two definitions, note that in a wff beginning with only existential quantifiers or with only universal quantifiers the scopes of which end in the same place, the succession of these quantifiers may be altered arbitrarily with the value of the wff remaining the same. This is easily seen by the valuation rule $V6$.

Examples: The wff

$$(z)(Eu)(Ev)(z=u \vee z=v \;\&\; \overline{u=v}) \;\&\; (G)(\overline{x=y} \vee Gxx \vee \overline{Gyy})$$

is valid in a domain with two elements, but not valid in a domain with one element, as was shown before.

The wff $\overline{x=y} \;\&\; \overline{x=z} \;\&\; \overline{y=z}$ is satisfiable in a domain with three elements, as may be shown by giving the valuation of $(Ex)(Ey)(Ez)(\overline{x=y} \;\&\; \overline{x=z} \;\&\; \overline{y=z})$ for such a domain.

# II

# THE DECISION PROBLEM

## 1. Valuation in arbitrary domains. Universal validity

In § 2 of the preceding chapter we gave a definition of validity and satisfiability of wffs in finite domains. We now proceed to define the *valuation of a wff for an arbitrary non-empty domain D*, the elements of which may be of infinite number. This does not require any change in the relative definitions. The notions of propositional function and of an assignment for the free variables of a wff remain the same as before. The only difference is that the number of the $n$-adic propositional functions over $D$ is infinite, if $D$ has an infinite number of elements. Likewise, the valuation rules $V1-V6$ remain unchanged as well as the notions of validity and satisfiability of a wff in a domain $D$. But now there may be an infinite number of assignments for individual variables and for predicate variables. Though the valuation of a wff is defined by the six rules $V1-V6$, these rules in general do not afford a procedure by which the valuation may be effectively carried out. For by $V6$, the valuation of a wff for a given assignment is in general reduced to the valuation of another wff for an infinite number of assignments.

*A wff is called universally valid, if it is valid in every non-empty domain. A wff is called satisfiable simply if there is a non-empty domain in which it is satisfiable.*

The definitions of validity and satisfiability, together with the valuation rules $V4$ and $V6$, immediately yield the following relations between these two concepts. If a wff $\mathfrak{A}$ containing free variables is not valid in a domain $D$, $\overline{\mathfrak{A}}$ is satisfiable in that domain, and conversely. If a wff $\mathfrak{A}$ with free variables is not universally valid, $\overline{\mathfrak{A}}$ is satisfiable, and vice versa.

Since for wffs with free variables each of the two concepts of validity and satisfiability, as well as each of the concepts of universal validity and simple satisfiability, may be reduced to the other, it is sufficient to treat one of them. In the subsequent chapters we shall occupy ourselves only with the validity of wffs, though in some respects the concept of satisfiability is more easily handled when interpreting the wffs. The reason is that the *semantic truth-definition* for wffs we have given here may then be more conveniently brought into connection with a syntactical truth-definition (cf. the preface).

A *syntactical truth-definition*, which is not given in this book, is relative to a certain system of axioms. Such a system contains stipulations declaring a special class of wffs (the axioms) to be universally valid. These stipulations further give prescriptions (deduction rules) for generating a new universally valid wff from a finite number of such wffs under certain conditions. A wff is provable in the system, if it is an axiom or if it may be generated from the set of axioms by a finite number of applications of the deduction rules. Syntactically true means provable. As the provable wffs are universally valid the notion of validity, but not that of satisfiability, has a direct connection with the syntactical truth-definition.

Even when using such a syntactical truth-definition a semantical truth-definition is not superfluous. For we must convince ourselves that the wffs called axioms are universally valid and that the deduction rules proceed from universally valid wffs to universally valid wffs, and that the wffs which are syntactically true really comprise all universally valid wffs. This can only be done by semantic methods.

For the total number of wffs regarded here, there is no system of axioms delivering all universally valid wffs. Moreover, we are not only interested in the universal validity of wffs. Systems of axioms yielding all universally valid wffs exist for special classes of wffs. Wffs forming such a class are 1) the wffs of the propositional calculus, i.e. the wffs containing only propositional variables as prime formulas, 2) the wffs containing no predicate variables (the wffs of the pure calculus of equality), 3) the wffs containing no bound predicate variables (the wffs of the predicate calculus of first order) wherein the wffs containing the sign of equality may be included or not, and wffs of other special classes.

We illustrate the notions of validity, satisfiability and universal validity by giving some examples.

(1) $$(Ey)(Gx \vee \overline{Gy})$$

This wff is universally valid; for if the element $a$ of an arbitrary domain $D$ is assigned to $x$ and any monadic propositional function over $D$ to $G$, the assignment $a$ for $y$ gives $Gx \vee \overline{Gy}$ the value $T$, since $Gx$ and $Gy$ get the same value.

(2) $$(EG)(x)(Ey)(Gxx \;\&\; \overline{Gxy}).$$

This formula is valid in a domain $D$ which contains at least two elements; it is not valid in domains with only one element. If there is only one element in $D$, $Gxx \;\&\; \overline{Gxy}$ gets the value $F$ by any assignment, since the elements assigned to $x$ and $y$ are the same. Consequently, the wff itself gets the value $F$. If there are at least two elements in $D$, we assign to $G$ the dyadic propositional function over $D$ the value of which is $T$ only for an ordered pair of elements of $D$, the first and second member of which are the same. Then, given any assignment for $x$, an assignment for $y$ can be found, namely an element of $D$ different from the element assigned to $x$, so that $Gxx \;\&\; \overline{Gxy}$ gets the value $T$, which means that $(EG)(x)(Ey)(Gxx \;\&\; \overline{Gxy})$ gets the value $T$.

(3) $$Gx \;\&\; \overline{Gy} \;\&\; x=y.$$

This wff is valid in no domain at all; it is not even satisfiable. For if we assign to $G$ an arbitrary monadic propositional function over a domain $D$ and the elements $a$ and $b$ of $D$ to $x$ and $y$, either $a$ and $b$ are not the same elements, in which case $x=y$ gets the value $F$, or $a$ and $b$ are the same elements; in this case, $Gx$ and $Gy$ get the same value, so that either $Gx$ or $\overline{Gy}$ gets the value $F$. In any case $Gx \;\&\; \overline{Gy} \;\&\; x=y$ gets the value $F$.

(4) $$(EG)((x)(Ey)Gxy \;\&\; (x)\overline{Gxx} \;\&\; (x)(y)(z)(\overline{Gxy} \vee \overline{Gyz} \vee Gxz))$$

This wff is valid in any domain having an infinite number of elements, and only in such a domain.

If $D$ has an infinite number of elements, there is a denumerably infinite subdomain of $D$ called $D_1$ with the elements $a_1, a_2, a_3, \ldots$. We assign to $G$ the dyadic propositional function over $D$ the value of which is $T$ only for the ordered pairs $(a_n, a_{n+k})$ $(k>0)$ and $(b, a_k)$ $(k \geqslant 1)$, $b$ not being an element of $D_1$. It is easy to see that by this assignment $(x)(Ey)Gxy$ & $(x)\overline{Gxx}$ & $(x)(y)(z)(\overline{Gxy} \vee \overline{Gyz} \vee Gxz)$ gets the value $T$, since each conjunction term gets the value $T$.

On the other hand, if $D$ has only a finite number of elements, let $\Phi$ be an arbitrary dyadic propositional function over $D$. There is a subdomain of $D$ having the following property $\mathfrak{P}$: If $a$ is an arbitrary element of the subdomain and the ordered pair $(a, b)$ gets the value $T$ by $\Phi$, then $b$ is an element of the subdomain also. For instance, $D$ itself is such a subdomain. Let $D_1$ be one of the subdomains with the property $\mathfrak{P}$ having the smallest number of elements. If $(x)(Ey)Gxy$ & $(x)\overline{Gxx}$ & $(x)(y)(z)(\overline{Gxy} \vee \overline{Gyz} \vee Gxz)$ is to get the value $T$ by assigning $\Phi$ to $G$ and if $c$ is some element of $D_1$, there is another element $c_1$ of $D_1$ not identical with $c$ such that $(c, c_1)$ gets the value $T$ by $\Phi$, since $(x)(Ey)Gxy$ & $(x)\overline{Gxx}$ is to have the value $T$. Let $D_2$ be the set of all these elements $c_1$. $D_2$ has a smaller number of elements than $D_1$. If $c_2$ is an arbitrary element of $D_2$ and if $b$ is an element of $D$ such that $(c_2, b)$ gets the value $T$ by $\Phi$, the value of $(c, b)$ for $\Phi$ is $T$, since we are supposing that $(x)(y)(z)(\overline{Gxy} \vee \overline{Gyz} \vee Gxz)$ gets the value $T$ by assigning $\Phi$ to $G$. Therefore, $b$ is an element of $D_2$. This means that $D_2$ also has the property $\mathfrak{P}$. Since $D_1$ was supposed to be one of the smallest subdomains of $D$ with the property $\mathfrak{P}$, this is a contradiction.Therefore our supposition that the wff gets the value $T$ by assigning $\Phi$ to $G$, cannot be true. Since $\Phi$ was arbitrary, our wff (4) gets the value $F$ in any finite domain.

## 2. Equivalences

If a wff $\mathfrak{A} \leftrightarrow \mathfrak{B}$, i.e. $\overline{\mathfrak{A}} \vee \mathfrak{B}$ & $\mathfrak{A} \vee \overline{\mathfrak{B}}$ is valid in a domain $D$, the valuations of $\mathfrak{A}$ and of $\mathfrak{B}$ are the same for two relative assignments which coincide with respect to the variables common to $\mathfrak{A}$ and $\mathfrak{B}$. For it is an immediate consequence of the valuation rules $V4$ and $V5$ that by any assignment $\mathfrak{A} \leftrightarrow \mathfrak{B}$ gets the value $T$, if and only if both $\mathfrak{A}$ and $\mathfrak{B}$ get the value $T$ by this assignment, or if both wffs get the value $F$.

If $\mathfrak{A} \leftrightarrow \mathfrak{B}$ is valid in $D$, if $\mathfrak{A}$ is part of a wff $\mathfrak{C}$ and if the wff $\mathfrak{C}_1$ is obtained from $\mathfrak{C}$ by replacing the part $\mathfrak{A}$ of $\mathfrak{C}$ by $\mathfrak{B}$ and by dropping, if necessary, vacuous quantifiers (those quantifiers the scopes of which do not contain the variable of the quantifier), $\mathfrak{C} \leftrightarrow \mathfrak{C}_1$ is valid in $D$, provided that $\mathfrak{B}$ contains no free variables not occurring in $\mathfrak{A}$. For it is clear that any assignment gives the same value to $\mathfrak{C}$ and $\mathfrak{C}_1$.

$\mathfrak{A}$ and $\mathfrak{B}$ are called *equivalent wffs*, if $\mathfrak{A} \leftrightarrow \mathfrak{B}$ is universally valid. If $\mathfrak{A}$ and $\mathfrak{B}$ are equivalent wffs and if $\mathfrak{C}$ and $\mathfrak{C}_1$ have the same meaning as before, $\mathfrak{C}$ and $\mathfrak{C}_1$ are equivalent wffs.

Equivalent wffs are valid or not valid in exactly the same domains.

In the following we state several equivalences which are used later on.

*E*1. From a wff $\mathfrak{A}$ we get an equivalent wff $\mathfrak{B}$ by the following transformation. The variable of a quantifier of $\mathfrak{A}$ and the same variable in all places of the scope of the quantifier is replaced by another variable of the same character. This transformation is restricted to the case in which $\mathfrak{B}$ is a wff and the newly introduced variable is not identical with one of the variables occurring in the scope of the quantifier.

Example: $(Ex)Gx$ & $(Ex)Gx$ may be transformed into $(Ex)Gx$ & & $(Ey)Gy$, and conversely.

Indeed, it is seen by *V*6 that by any assignment for the free variables of $\mathfrak{A}$ in any domain the part of $\mathfrak{A}$ consisting of the quantifier and its scope gets the same value $T$ or $F$ before and after the transformation, as does $\mathfrak{A}$.

If a wff $\mathfrak{A}$ is transformed in the described way one or more times we shall say that we have *rewritten the bound variables of* $\mathfrak{A}$.

Subsequently we shall not make much use of the syntactical variables $\mathfrak{a}, \mathfrak{b}, \mathfrak{c}, \ldots, \mathfrak{U}, \mathfrak{V}, \mathfrak{W}, \ldots$, and $\mathfrak{U}^n, \mathfrak{V}^n, \mathfrak{W}^n, \ldots$, which stand respectively for any individual variable, any propositional variable and for any $n$-adic predicate variable. A statement, for instance, concerning the validity of some wff $(x)(Ey)(z)\mathfrak{A}(x, y, z)$ equally holds for any wff $(\mathfrak{a})(E\mathfrak{b})(\mathfrak{c})\mathfrak{A}(\mathfrak{a}, \mathfrak{b}, \mathfrak{c})$ resulting from $(x)(Ey)(z)\mathfrak{A}(x,y,z)$ by rewriting the bound variables. Therefore it is sufficient to state such statements for specially chosen bound variables.

In stating the equivalences $E5-E16$ $\mathfrak{a}$ may designate individual variables as well as propositional variables and predicate variables, since these equivalences hold for all kinds of variables. Pairs of equivalent wffs are the following ones:

$$
\begin{array}{lllll}
E2. & \overline{\overline{\mathfrak{A}}} & \text{and} & \mathfrak{A}; \\
E3. & \overline{\mathfrak{A} \,\&\, \mathfrak{B}} & \text{and} & \overline{\mathfrak{A}} \vee \overline{\mathfrak{B}}; \\
E4. & \overline{\mathfrak{A} \vee \mathfrak{B}} & \text{and} & \overline{\mathfrak{A}} \,\&\, \overline{\mathfrak{B}}; \\
E5. & \overline{(\mathfrak{a})\mathfrak{A}(\mathfrak{a})} & \text{and} & (E\mathfrak{a})\overline{\mathfrak{A}(\mathfrak{a})}; \\
E6. & \overline{(E\mathfrak{a})\mathfrak{A}(\mathfrak{a})} & \text{and} & (\mathfrak{a})\overline{\mathfrak{A}(\mathfrak{a})}; \\
E7. & (E\mathfrak{a})(\mathfrak{A}(\mathfrak{a}) \vee \mathfrak{B}(\mathfrak{a})) & \text{and} & (E\mathfrak{a})\mathfrak{A}(\mathfrak{a}) \vee (E\mathfrak{a})\mathfrak{B}(\mathfrak{a}); \\
E8. & (\mathfrak{a})(\mathfrak{A}(\mathfrak{a}) \,\&\, \mathfrak{B}(\mathfrak{a})) & \text{and} & (\mathfrak{a})\mathfrak{A}(\mathfrak{a}) \,\&\, (\mathfrak{a})\mathfrak{B}(\mathfrak{a}); \\
E9. & (E\mathfrak{a})\mathfrak{A}(\mathfrak{a}) \,\&\, \mathfrak{B} & \text{and} & (E\mathfrak{a})(\mathfrak{A}(\mathfrak{a}) \,\&\, \mathfrak{B}); \\
E10. & \mathfrak{B} \,\&\, (E\mathfrak{a})\mathfrak{A}(\mathfrak{a}) & \text{and} & (E\mathfrak{a})(\mathfrak{B} \,\&\, \mathfrak{A}(\mathfrak{a})); \\
E11. & (E\mathfrak{a})\mathfrak{A}(\mathfrak{a}) \vee \mathfrak{B} & \text{and} & (E\mathfrak{a})(\mathfrak{A}(\mathfrak{a}) \vee \mathfrak{B}); \\
E12. & \mathfrak{B} \vee (E\mathfrak{a})\mathfrak{A}(\mathfrak{a}) & \text{and} & (E\mathfrak{a})(\mathfrak{B} \vee \mathfrak{A}(\mathfrak{a})); \\
E13. & (\mathfrak{a})\mathfrak{A}(\mathfrak{a}) \,\&\, \mathfrak{B} & \text{and} & (\mathfrak{a})(\mathfrak{A}(\mathfrak{a}) \,\&\, \mathfrak{B}); \\
E14. & \mathfrak{B} \,\&\, (\mathfrak{a})\mathfrak{A}(\mathfrak{a}) & \text{and} & (\mathfrak{a})(\mathfrak{B} \,\&\, \mathfrak{A}(\mathfrak{a})); \\
E15. & (\mathfrak{a})\mathfrak{A}(\mathfrak{a}) \vee \mathfrak{B} & \text{and} & (\mathfrak{a})(\mathfrak{A}(\mathfrak{a}) \vee \mathfrak{B}); \\
E16. & \mathfrak{B} \vee (\mathfrak{a})\mathfrak{A}(\mathfrak{a}) & \text{and} & (\mathfrak{a})(\mathfrak{B} \vee \mathfrak{A}(\mathfrak{a})); \\
E17. & (x)(\overline{x=y} \vee \mathfrak{A}(x, y)) & \text{and} & \mathfrak{A}(y, y); \\
E18. & (Ex)(x=y \,\&\, \mathfrak{A}(x, y)) & \text{and} & \mathfrak{A}(y, y).
\end{array}
$$

The equivalences $E2-E16$ are an immediate consequence of the valuation rules $V1-V6$. In $E9-E16$, the wff $\mathfrak{B}$ of course cannot contain the variable $\mathfrak{a}$, because we have assumed that we have a pair of wffs. In $E17$ and $E18$, $\mathfrak{A}(y, y)$ is the wff resulting from $\mathfrak{A}(x, y)$ by substituting $y$ for $x$ in all places where $x$ occurs. The pairs of wffs mentioned in $E17$ and $E18$ are recognized as pairs of equivalent wffs as follows. If we have an assignment for the free variables of $\mathfrak{A}(y, y)$ in a domain $D$ and an assignment for $\mathfrak{A}(x, y)$ which is the same as that for $\mathfrak{A}(y, y)$ for the variables different from $x$, and by which the same element of $D$ is assigned to $x$ and to $y$, then these assignments give the same value to $\mathfrak{A}(y, y)$ and to

$\mathfrak{A}(x, y)$. This is clear for prime formulas and may be proven for other wffs by induction, according to the construction of wffs by $W1 - W6$ of Chapter I, § 1. If an assignment for the free variables of $\mathfrak{A}(y, y)$ is given, this assignment gives the same value to $(Ex)(x=y \;\&\; \mathfrak{A}(x, y))$. For if $\mathfrak{A}(y, y)$ gets the value $T$ by this assignment, so does $x=y \;\&\; \mathfrak{A}(x, y)$, provided the assignment is completed by assigning to $x$ the same element as to $y$. If $\mathfrak{A}(y, y)$ gets the value $F$ by this assignment, $x=y \;\&\; \mathfrak{A}(x, y)$ also receives the value $F$ by any assignment coinciding with the assignment for $\mathfrak{A}(y, y)$ with respect to the variables different from $x$. This results from what we have said above if the same element is assigned to $x$ and $y$. If different elements are assigned to $x$ and to $y$, $x=y$ and therefore $x=y \;\&\; \mathfrak{A}(x, y)$ get the value $F$. In a similar manner it is to be seen that $\mathfrak{A}(y, y)$ and $(x)(\overline{x=y} \vee \mathfrak{A}(x, y))$ are equivalent wffs.

*E*19. A disjunction $\mathfrak{A}_1 \vee \ldots \vee \mathfrak{A}_n$ is transformed into an equivalent wff if the succession of the disjunction terms is somehow altered. The analogous statement is true for a conjunction.

*E*20. The wffs $\mathfrak{A}$ and $\mathfrak{A} \;\&\; \mathfrak{B}$ are equivalent if $\mathfrak{B}$ is universally valid. The wffs $\mathfrak{A}$ and $\mathfrak{A} \vee \mathfrak{B}$ are equivalent, if $\mathfrak{B}$ is not satisfiable in any domain, i.e. if $\overline{\mathfrak{B}}$ is universally valid.

*E*21. The wffs $\mathfrak{A} \vee (\mathfrak{B} \;\&\; \mathfrak{C})$ and $\mathfrak{A} \vee \mathfrak{B} \;\&\; \mathfrak{A} \vee \mathfrak{C}$ as well as the wffs $\mathfrak{A} \;\&\; \mathfrak{B} \vee \mathfrak{C}$ and $(\mathfrak{A} \;\&\; \mathfrak{B}) \vee (\mathfrak{A} \;\&\; \mathfrak{C})$ are equivalent wffs.

*E*19—*E*21 are easily recognized to be true by the valuation rules.

## 3. *S*-formulas. Elimination of the propositional variables

We often have to form sentences like this: "A wff gets the value $T$ or $F$ if the element $a$ is assigned to $x$, the element $b$ to $y$, the monadic propositional function $\Psi$ to $G^1$, etc." It is desirable to have a shorter form for such statements; this will be obtained as follows. Instead of saying "$x=y \;\&\; (z)Gxz$ gets the value $T(F)$, if we assign $a$ to $x$, $b$ to $y$ and $\Phi$ to $G$", we use in a synonymous manner the sentence", $a=b \;\&\; (z)\Phi az$ is true (false)". Likewise, "$X \vee Y \;\&\; (G)(Gx \vee Gy)$ gets the value $F$, if we assign $T$ to $X$, $F$ to $Y$, $a$ to $x$, and $a$ to $y$" and "$T \vee F \;\&\; (G)(Ga \vee Ga)$ is false" shall have the same sense. By this we do not intend to extend the notion of wff. Formal expressions like $T \vee F \;\&\; (G)(Ga \vee Ga)$ only occur in statements about wffs; they do not belong to our formal language. We shall call such formal expressions *S*-formulas.

*S-formulas* are those, and only those, formal expressions which result from a wff with free variables by replacing all or some of these variables by the names of things assigned to them in a domain. The replacement of a free variable must be done in all places where it occurs. Wffs without free variables may also occur among the *S*-formulas. If an *S*-formula results from a wff in this way, we say that the *S*-formula belongs to the wff and the assignment for the free variables of the wff. The wff and the assignment to which an *S*-formula belongs, is not uniquely determined by the *S*-formula, even if we disregard the fact that different letters may be used for the free variables of the wff. E.g. $a=a$ belongs to $x=x$ and the assignment $a$ for $x$, but also to $x=y$ and the assignment $a$ for $x$ and $a$ for $y$. $T \vee \overline{T} \,\&\, Z$ belongs to $X \vee \overline{X} \,\&\, Z$ and the assignment $T$ for $X$, but also to $Y \vee \overline{X} \,\&\, Z$ and the assignment $T$ for $X$ and $T$ for $Y$ (but not to $Z \vee \overline{Z} \,\&\, Z$).

The same *S*-formula may belong to a wff $\mathfrak{A}$ and an assignment $\Omega_1$ and to a wff $\mathfrak{B}$ and the assignment $\Omega_2$ which is relative to the same domain as $\Omega_1$. $\mathfrak{A}$ and $\mathfrak{B}$ can only differ in such a way that the place for a variable in $\mathfrak{A}$ is occupied by another variable of the same character in $\mathfrak{B}$. Variables in corresponding places of $\mathfrak{A}$ and $\mathfrak{B}$ get, if any, the same assignments by $\Omega_1$ and $\Omega_2$. If two places are occupied by the same variable in one wff and the corresponding places in the other wff by different variables, then the assignment for the two variables of the second wff is the same. $\Omega_1$ and $\Omega_2$ give the same value to $\mathfrak{A}$ and to $\mathfrak{B}$ if they are complete assignments and otherwise, if their completion is achieved by adding the same assignments for the other free variables. This is seen at once for prime formulas by inspecting the valuation rules $V1-V3$ and is proved for other wffs by induction according to $V4-V6$. Thus the statement "An *S*-formula is true in a domain $D$" has sense without naming a special wff to which the *S*-formula belongs. "An *S*-formula without free variables is true (false) in a domain $D$" is only another expression for "The *S*-formula belongs to a wff and an assignment for its free variables over $D$ which gives the wff the value $T(F)$", or

"Any wff and pertaining assignment gives the wff the value $T(F)$ in $D$ if the $S$-formula belongs to them". "An $S$-formula with free variables is true (false) in $D$ for an assignment for the free variables" means "The $S$-formula belongs to a wff and an assignment for a part of the free variables of the wff over $D$ which, completed by assigning to the other free variables the same things as to the free variables of the $S$-formula identical with them, gives the wff the value $T(F)$ in $D$". Note that not for every assignment for the free variables of an $S$-formula in an arbitrary domain the formula is true or false, since this assignment must be made up to form a complete assignment with the assignment to which the $S$-formula belongs. The $S$-formula $\Psi xx$, for instance, can be true or false only if an element of the domain $D$ over which $\Psi$ is defined, is assigned to $x$. $a = x$ & $Gax$ is true or false only for assignments for $x$ and $G$ in domains of which $a$ is an element.

Two $S$-formulas $\mathfrak{S}_1$ and $\mathfrak{S}_2$ are called equivalent if $\mathfrak{S}_1 \leftrightarrow \mathfrak{S}_2$ is true in every domain for all assignments for the free variables of $\mathfrak{S}_1 \leftrightarrow \mathfrak{S}_2$. For wffs this notion of equivalence is the same as that given in § 2 of this chapter. $\mathfrak{S}_3$ and $\mathfrak{S}_4$ are equivalent $S$-formulas if the following conditions are fulfilled: $\mathfrak{S}_1$ and $\mathfrak{S}_2$ are equivalent $S$-formulas; $\mathfrak{S}_2$ does not contain any free variables not occurring in $\mathfrak{S}_1$; $\mathfrak{S}_1$ is part of an $S$-formula $\mathfrak{S}_3$; the $S$-formula $\mathfrak{S}_4$ results from $\mathfrak{S}_3$ by replacing the part $\mathfrak{S}_1$ of $\mathfrak{S}_3$ by $\mathfrak{S}_2$ and by dropping, if necessary, quantifiers which have become superfluous.

If a wff is equivalent to the $S$-formula $T(F)$, then the wff is universally valid (valid in no domain at all).

*As is seen by the definition of equivalence, this notion is restricted to S-formulas containing only T and F besides the primitive symbols of wffs.* Such $S$-formulas can be transformed into equivalent wffs or into one of the two $S$-formulas, $T$ or $F$. This is done by replacing in the $S$-formula, beginning anywhere, $\overline{T}$ by $F$, $\overline{F}$ by $T$, $T \vee \mathfrak{A}$ and $\mathfrak{A} \vee T$ by $T$, $F \vee \mathfrak{A}$ and $\mathfrak{A} \vee F$ by $\mathfrak{A}$, $T$ & $\mathfrak{A}$ and $\mathfrak{A}$ & $T$ by $\mathfrak{A}$, $F$ & $\mathfrak{A}$ and $\mathfrak{A}$ & $F$ by $F$ and by simultaneously dropping vacuous quantifiers, if necessary. Since all the mentioned pairs of $S$-formulas are pairs of equivalent $S$-formulas, the $S$-formula is transformed into an equivalent one. Since each reduction step diminishes the number of logical constants, this reduction can be carried on until $T$ and $F$ have disappeared from the $S$-formula, or until the $S$-formula is reduced to $T$ or to $F$.

This may be used to show that we need not investigate the validity or satisfiability of wffs containing propositional variables, because the propositional variables can be eliminated from a wff. Validity or satisfiability of a wff always means the validity of a certain wff containing no free variables. *A wff with bound propositional variables may always be replaced by an equivalent wff containing no propositional variables, or it may be recognized at once as universally valid or valid in no domain at all.*

Each such wff can at first be transformed into an equivalent $S$-formula without bound propositional variables by replacing in the wff, beginning at an arbitrary point, every part $(X)\mathfrak{A}(X)$ by $\mathfrak{A}(T)\ \&\ \mathfrak{A}(F)$ and every part $(EX)\mathfrak{A}(X)$ by $\mathfrak{A}(T) \vee \mathfrak{A}(F)$. This $S$-formula is then reduced in the way described above. If the formula resulting in the end is $T$ or $F$, the wff is universally valid or valid in no domain at all; otherwise, we get an equivalent wff without propositional variables.

The well-known truth-table decision procedure for wffs of the propositional calculus, i.e. for wffs containing no individual and no predicate variables, is included herein.

As an example we consider the wff:

$$(X)(X \vee (y)(\overline{y=y} \vee \overline{X}))\ \&\ (EY)(Y\ \&\ (EG)(Ex)(Gx\ \&\ Y)).$$

We first replace

$$(X)(X \vee (y)(\overline{y=y} \vee \overline{X})) \text{ by } T \vee (y)(\overline{y=y} \vee \overline{T})\ \&\ F \vee (y)(\overline{y=y} \vee \overline{F})$$

which reduces to $T$, so that the wff itself is reduced to

$$(EY)(Y\ \&\ (EG)(Ex)(Gx\ \&\ Y)).$$

We replace this wff by

$$(T\ \&\ (EG)(Ex)(Gx\ \&\ T)) \vee (F\ \&\ (EG)(Ex)(Gx\ \&\ F))$$

which reduces to $(EG)(Ex)Gx$. $(EG)(Ex)Gx$ is equivalent to the wff from which we were starting.

## 4. Normal forms

For this section we need the concept of $P$-constituent of a wff defined in § 1 of Chapter I.

A wff is said to express a *tautology*, or to be *tautologous*, if every $S$-formula reduces to $T$ which results from the wff by replacing the $P$-constituents in an arbitrary way by $T$ or $F$, but so that equally shaped $P$-constituents are replaced by the same letter.

A tautologous wff is of course universally valid, but not every universally valid wff is tautologous. E.g. $(x)(x=x)$ and $(x)(Gx \vee \overline{Gx})$ are universally valid, but not tautologous. Two tautologous wffs are equivalent.

Every wff can be brought into certain normal forms by means of equivalence transformations. There are several normal forms.

A wff is said to be in *conjunctive normal form* if it is a disjunction the terms of which are $P$-constituents or the negations of $P$-constituents of the wff or if it is a conjunction of such disjunctions. Wffs which consist only of one $P$-constituent or of the negation of a $P$-constituent shall be included among the above disjunctions.

We first show that for every non-tautologous wff an equivalent wff in conjunctive normal form can be constructed. $\mathfrak{A}_1, \mathfrak{A}_2, \ldots, \mathfrak{A}_n$ may be the $P$-constituents of the wff, $P$-constituents equally shaped not being counted twice. We will designate the wff by $\mathfrak{B}(\mathfrak{A}_1, \ldots, \mathfrak{A}_n)$. $\mathfrak{B}(T, \mathfrak{A}_2, \ldots, \mathfrak{A}_n)$ and $\mathfrak{B}(F, \mathfrak{A}_2, \ldots, \mathfrak{A}_n)$ are the $S$-formulas resulting from $\mathfrak{B}(\mathfrak{A}_1, \ldots, \mathfrak{A}_n)$ by replacing $\mathfrak{A}_1$ everywhere by $T(F)$.

$\mathfrak{B}(\mathfrak{A}_1, \ldots, \mathfrak{A}_n)$ is equivalent to the $S$-formula

$$\mathfrak{A}_1 \vee \mathfrak{B}(F, \mathfrak{A}_2, \ldots, \mathfrak{A}_n) \;\&\; \overline{\mathfrak{A}_1} \vee \mathfrak{B}(T, \mathfrak{A}_2, \ldots, \mathfrak{A}_n).$$

For if by any assignment $\mathfrak{A}_1$ gets the value $F$, then the $S$-formula gets the same value by this assignment as

$$F \vee \mathfrak{B}(F, \mathfrak{A}_2, \ldots, \mathfrak{A}_n) \;\&\; \overline{F} \vee \mathfrak{B}(T, \mathfrak{A}_2, \ldots, \mathfrak{A}_n).$$

This formula reduces to $\mathfrak{B}(F, \mathfrak{A}_2, \ldots, \mathfrak{A}_n)$ which gets the same value as $\mathfrak{B}(\mathfrak{A}_1, \ldots, \mathfrak{A}_n)$. If by any assignment $\mathfrak{A}_1$ gets the value $T$, the $S$-formula gets the same value as

$$T \vee \mathfrak{B}(F, \mathfrak{A}_2, \ldots, \mathfrak{A}_n) \;\&\; \overline{T} \vee \mathfrak{B}(T, \mathfrak{A}_2, \ldots, \mathfrak{A}_n),$$

which reduces to $\mathfrak{B}(T, \mathfrak{A}_2, \ldots, \mathfrak{A}_n)$.

We shall prove our theorem by induction on the number $n$ of $P$-constituents. If this number is one, $\mathfrak{B}(\mathfrak{A}_1)$ is equivalent to $\mathfrak{A}_1 \vee \mathfrak{B}(F) \;\&\; \overline{\mathfrak{A}_1} \vee \mathfrak{B}(T)$. We eliminate $T$ and $F$ in this $S$-formula by the methods of § 3 and get either $\mathfrak{A}_1$, or $\overline{\mathfrak{A}_1}$ or $\mathfrak{A}_1 \;\&\; \overline{\mathfrak{A}_1}$ as conjunctive normal form, since $\mathfrak{B}(F)$ and $\mathfrak{B}(T)$ cannot both reduce to $T$; otherwise $\mathfrak{B}(\mathfrak{A}_1)$ would be tautologous. Let us assume that we have shown our theorem to be true for a wff with less than $n$ $P$-constituents. $\mathfrak{B}(\mathfrak{A}_1, \ldots, \mathfrak{A}_n)$ is equivalent to

$$\mathfrak{A}_1 \vee \mathfrak{B}(F, \mathfrak{A}_2, \ldots, \mathfrak{A}_n) \;\&\; \overline{\mathfrak{A}_1} \vee \mathfrak{B}(T, \mathfrak{A}_2, \ldots, \mathfrak{A}_n)$$

In this $S$-formula $F$ and $T$ are again eliminated by the methods of § 3. The result is a wff of one of the following forms:

$$\mathfrak{A}_1 \vee \mathfrak{C} \;\&\; \overline{\mathfrak{A}_1} \vee \mathfrak{D},\ \mathfrak{A}_1 \vee \mathfrak{C} \;\&\; \overline{\mathfrak{A}_1},\ \mathfrak{A}_1 \vee \mathfrak{C},$$
$$\mathfrak{A}_1 \;\&\; \overline{\mathfrak{A}_1} \vee \mathfrak{D},\ \overline{\mathfrak{A}_1} \vee \mathfrak{D},\ \mathfrak{A}_1 \;\&\; \overline{\mathfrak{A}_1},\ \mathfrak{A}_1,\ \overline{\mathfrak{A}_1}.$$

The wff cannot reduce to $F$, as is seen by its structure; it cannot reduce to $T$, for in that case both $\mathfrak{B}(F, \mathfrak{A}_2, \ldots, \mathfrak{A}_n)$ and $\mathfrak{B}(T, \mathfrak{A}_2, \ldots, \mathfrak{A}_n)$ would reduce to $T$, which is impossible since $\mathfrak{B}(\mathfrak{A}_1, \mathfrak{A}_2, \ldots, \mathfrak{A}_n)$ is not tautologous. The last three of the above eight wffs are in conjunctive normal form. In the other five wffs, $\mathfrak{C}$ and $\mathfrak{D}$ are wffs with only the $P$-constituents $\mathfrak{A}_2, \ldots, \mathfrak{A}_n$ which according to our assumption can be brought into conjunctive normal forms $\mathfrak{C}'$ and $\mathfrak{D}'$. Because $\mathfrak{A}_1 \vee \mathfrak{C}'$ and $\overline{\mathfrak{A}_1} \vee \mathfrak{D}'$ can be transformed into a conjunctive normal form by means of the first equivalence $E21$ of § 2, this holds too for the five wffs. This completes our induction.

A tautologous wff with the $P$-constituents $\mathfrak{A}_1, \ldots, \mathfrak{A}_n$ can also be given a conjunctive normal form; e.g. $\mathfrak{A}_1 \vee \overline{\mathfrak{A}_1}$ is such a form.

A wff is in *disjunctive normal form* if it is a conjunction of $P$-constituents and the negations of $P$-constituents or if it is a disjunction of such conjunctions. Wffs consisting only of one $P$-constituent or of the negation of a $P$-constituent shall be included among the above conjunctions.

In order to show that a wff $\mathfrak{A}$ can always be brought into an equivalent disjunctive normal form, we first construct a conjunctive normal form $\mathfrak{B}_1 \;\&\; \ldots \;\&\; \mathfrak{B}_m$ of $\overline{\mathfrak{A}}$. According to $E2$ of § 2, $\mathfrak{A}$ is equivalent to $\overline{\overline{\mathfrak{A}}}$ and therefore to $\overline{\mathfrak{B}_1 \;\&\; \ldots \;\&\; \mathfrak{B}_m}$. Using $E3$,

$\overline{\mathfrak{B}_1 \,\&\, \dots \,\&\, \mathfrak{B}_m}$ is transformed into $\overline{\mathfrak{B}_1} \vee \dots \vee \overline{\mathfrak{B}_m}$. By $E4$ every $\overline{\mathfrak{B}_i}$ is transformed into a conjunction whose terms are negations of $P$-constituents or double negated $P$-constituents. By eliminating the double negations according to $E2$, we get a disjunctive normal form of $\mathfrak{A}$.

*Every wff can be given an equivalent normal form in which the negation-bar stands only over prime formulas.*

If a wff is given, by successive applications of $E3$, $E4$, $E5$ and $E6$ the negation signs can be brought farther and farther inside until finally they stand, one or more times, only over the prime formulas. By means of $E2$ the negation signs over the prime formulas are removed until there is at most one left.

Example: The wff

$$\overline{(G)(Ex)(Ey)(Gxy \,\&\, \overline{\overline{x=y}})} \text{ becomes } (EG)(x)(y)(\overline{Gxy} \vee x=y)$$

by the transformation.

*We may further transform any wff into an equivalent one in which the quantifiers occur only at the beginning with scopes extending to the end of the wff, no quantifier standing under a negation-bar.*

We first transform the given wff into one in which the negation-bars stand at most over prime formulas. Then we rewrite the bound variables (see $E1$ of § 2) in a way such that all quantifiers have different variables. Subsequently, we place all the quantifiers at the beginning of the wff with scopes extending to the end of the wff, by using several times the equivalences $E9$—$E16$ of § 2. This generally can be done in more than one way. For instance, the quantifiers can be placed at the beginning of the wff in the order in which they occur, but also any succession of the initially placed quantifiers can be obtained such that any quantifier which was in the scope of another quantifier remains in the scope of that quantifier.

A wff in which all the quantifiers are placed at the beginning of the wff with scopes extending to the end of the wff is said to be in a *prenex normal form*. The succession of quantifiers with which the wff begins is called the *prefix* of the wff. The part of the wff which remains if all the quantifiers are deleted is called the *matrix* of the wff.

Example: A prenex normal form of $\overline{(x)(Ey)Gxy} \mathbin{\&} (Ez)Hz$ is $(Ex)(y)(Ez)(\overline{Gxy} \mathbin{\&} Hz)$ with the prefix $(Ex)(y)(Ez)$ and the matrix $\overline{Gxy} \mathbin{\&} Hz$. Other prenex normal forms are $(Ex)(Ez)(y)(\overline{Gxy} \mathbin{\&} Hz)$ and $(Ez)(Ex)(y)(\overline{Gxy} \mathbin{\&} Hz)$.

## 5. Three forms of the decision problem

If a wff is valid (satisfiable) in a domain $D$, it is also valid (satisfiable) in a domain $D_1$ which has the same cardinal number as $D$, i.e. the elements of which may be put into one-to-one correspondence with those of $D$. Indeed, through the assignment used for the valuation of a wff in $D$, there may be determined in an unambigous way assignments relative to $D_1$ which give the same valuation. If $a$ is assigned to an individual variable relative to $D$, the corresponding element $a_1$ of $D_1$ is used for the assignment relative to $D_1$. If the $n$-adic propositional function $\Phi$ is assigned to $\mathfrak{U}^n$ in $D$, the assignment for $\mathfrak{U}^n$ relative to $D_1$ is the propositional function $\Phi_1$ over $D_1$ which assigns the value $T$ to those, and only those, $n$-tuples $(b_1, \ldots, b_n)$ over $D_1$ for which $\Phi$ gives the value $T$ to the corresponding $n$-tuples $(a_1, \ldots, a_n)$ over $D$, $a_i$ corresponding to $b_i$.

*Therefore, disregarding those wffs which are universally valid (satisfiable in every non-empty domain) and disregarding those which have this property in no domain, the assertion of the validity (or satisfiability) of a wff in a domain D is equivalent to a statement about the cardinal number of D.*

The definition of validity does not supply us with a criterion for recognizing in the general case whether a given wff is valid (satisfiable) in a given domain, or whether it is universally valid (satisfiable) at all. The problem of finding an effective procedure for determining the validity (satisfiability) of a given wff is called the *decision problem*. More precisely, as the validity and satisfiability of a wff depend on the cardinal number of the relative domain, the decision problem may be stated in several distinct forms. We formulate all of them with respect to the problem of validity, since this is sufficient (see § 1 of this chapter).

The most important form is this:

I. *To decide for a given wff whether it is universally valid or not.*

A more comprising form of the problem is this:

II. *To decide for a given wff whether it is universally valid. If it is not universally valid, to decide whether it is valid in no domain whatsoever or in some domain. In the last case the cardinal numbers of the domains for which it is valid are to be determined.*

Other forms of the decision problem may be stated as well, e.g. the following one:

III. *To decide for a given wff whether it is valid in all domains with a finite number of elements or not.*

As far as the literature goes nearly all investigations about soluble cases of the decision problem concern problems I and II; III has been dealt with only in connection with II, since a solution of II includes a solution of III (but see § 2 of chapter VIII).

Of course it would be most desirable to have a decision procedure applicable to all wffs. Investigations made at first by A. Church [1, 2], then by A. Turing [1] and others, by which the somewhat vague intuitive notion of a decision procedure was replaced by a precise definition, show that a general solution of the decision problem in the forms I and II cannot be found. B. A. Trachtenbrod [1] has shown also that a general solution of the form III of the decision problem is not possible. To enter into the particulars of these investigations is outside the limits of this book.

It remains to look for a solution of the problem for special cases, i.e. for certain special well-defined classes of wffs. In the following we give a survey of the more important special cases for which a solution has hitherto been reached.

III

# SOLUTION OF THE DECISION PROBLEM FOR EQUALITY FORMULAS

In this chapter we give a solution of the decision problem for wffs which contain no predicate variables, but only individual variables. The prime formulas of such wffs are all of the form $\mathfrak{a}=\mathfrak{b}$. We will call those formulas for short *equality formulas*. This problem seems to have been solved first, in connection with the more comprehensive problem of chapter IV, by L. Löwenheim [1]. We give here an independent treatment.

## 1. Solution of the form II of the decision problem

It is sufficient to give a decision procedure for wffs in prenex normal form. Let $\mathfrak{A}(x_1, \ldots, x_m)$ be such a wff with the free variables $x_1, \ldots, x_m$ and with a prefix consisting of $n$ quantifiers. Further, let $k$ be $m+n$. We have the following theorem:

*If $\mathfrak{A}$ is valid in a domain with $k$ elements, it is also valid in any domain with more than $k$ elements. If $\mathfrak{A}$ is valid in some domain with more than $k$ elements, it is also valid in a domain with $k$ elements.*

We prove a furthergoing theorem. Let $D_k$ be a domain with $k$ elements and $D$ one with more than $k$ elements. $a_1, \ldots, a_m$ and $b_1, \ldots, b_m$ may be $m$-tuples of elements of $D_k(D)$ such that a one-to-one correspondence can be established between $a_1, \ldots, a_m$ and $b_1, \ldots, b_m$, each $a_i$ corresponding to $b_i$. We may also say equivalently that these elements fulfill the following condition: For each $p$ and $q$, $a_p$ and $a_q$ are identical, if and only if $b_p$ and $b_q$ are identical. Under these conditions $\mathfrak{A}(a_1, \ldots, a_m)$ is true in $D_k$ if $\mathfrak{A}(b_1, \ldots, b_m)$ is in $D$, and vice versa.

This includes the theorem above. For if $\mathfrak{A}(x_1, \ldots, x_m)$ is valid in $D_k$, then $\mathfrak{A}(a_1, \ldots, a_m)$ is true in $D_k$ for arbitrarily chosen elements $a_1, \ldots, a_m$ of $D_k$. If $b_1, \ldots, b_m$ are arbitrary elements of $D$, we can find elements $a_1, \ldots, a_m$ of $D_k$ satisfying the above-mentioned conditions between $a_i$ and $b_i$, since $k \geqslant m$. $\mathfrak{A}(b_1, \ldots, b_m)$ is then always true in $D$. Likewise, if $\mathfrak{A}(b_1, \ldots, b_m)$ is true in $D$ for arbitrary elements $b_1, \ldots, b_m$ of $D$, $\mathfrak{A}(a_1, \ldots, a_m)$ is always true in $D_k$, for we can establish a one-to-one correspondence between given elements $a_1, \ldots, a_m$ and certain elements $b_1, \ldots, b_m$ of $D$.

The second theorem is proved for an arbitrary $k$ by induction on the number $n$ of the quantifiers of $\mathfrak{A}(x_1, \ldots, x_m)$. If $n$ is 0, the theorem is evident, since all the prime formulas of $\mathfrak{A}(x_1, \ldots, x_m)$ are of the form $x_p = x_q$ and since $a_p = a_q$ and $b_p = b_q$ are supposed to be both true or both false. We assume the theorem to be proven for $n$ quantifiers. If $\mathfrak{A}(x_1, \ldots, x_m)$ has $n+1$ quantifiers, it either has a form $(y)\mathfrak{B}(y, x_1, \ldots, x_m)$ or $(Ey)\mathfrak{B}(y, x_1, \ldots, x_m)$. $a_1, \ldots, a_m$ and $b_1, \ldots, b_m$ may be $m$-tuples of elements of $D_k$ and $D$ fulfilling the condition expressed in the theorem. If $(y)\mathfrak{B}(y, a_1, \ldots, a_m)$ is true in $D_k$, $\mathfrak{B}(c, a_1, \ldots, a_m)$ is true in $D_k$ however the element $c$ may be chosen in $D_k$. Now take an arbitrary element $d$ of $D$. We select an element $c_1$ of $D_k$ which is identical with $a_i$, if $d$ is identical with $b_i$, and which is different from all the elements $a_1, \ldots, a_m$, if $d$ is different from every $b_i$. Such an element $c_1$ can be found in $D_k$, since $k \geqslant m+1$. Because $\mathfrak{B}(c_1, a_1, \ldots, a_m)$ is true in $D_k$, $\mathfrak{B}(d, b_1, \ldots, b_m)$ is true in $D$, since $\mathfrak{B}$ has only $n$ quantifiers. Since $d$ was arbitrary, $(y)\,\mathfrak{B}(y, b_1, \ldots, b_m)$ is true in $D$.

If $(y)\mathfrak{B}(y, b_1, \ldots, b_m)$ is true in $D$, $\mathfrak{B}(d, b_1, \ldots, b_m)$ is true for an arbitrary $d$ of $D$; then $\mathfrak{B}(c, a_1, \ldots, a_m)$ is true in $D_k$ for an arbitrary $c$. For we can find an element $d_1$ of $D$ such that $d_1, b_1, \ldots, b_m$ and $c, a_1, \ldots, a_m$ are in one-to-one correspondence, since $D$ has more elements than $D_k$. Since $\mathfrak{B}(d_1, b_1, \ldots, b_m)$ is true, $\mathfrak{B}(c, a_1, \ldots, a_m)$ is also true, which means that $(y)\mathfrak{B}(y, a_1, \ldots, a_m)$ is true in $D_k$.

If $(Ey)\mathfrak{B}(y, a_1, \ldots, a_m)$ is true in $D_k$, this means that there is an element $c$ of $D_k$ such that $\mathfrak{B}(c, a_1, \ldots, a_m)$ is true. Using a similar argumentation as before, we can find an element $d$ of $D$ such that $d, b_1, \ldots, b_m$ and $c, a_1, \ldots, a_m$ can be put into one-to-one correspondence. By our supposition $(Ey)\mathfrak{B}(y, b_1, \ldots, b_m)$ is true in $D$. If $(Ey)\mathfrak{B}(y, b_1, \ldots, b_m)$ is true in $D$, $(Ey)\mathfrak{B}(y, a_1, \ldots, a_m)$ is true in $D_k$. This is proven by the same method.

Since our induction is thus complete, the second theorem and therefore the first one, the only one in which we are interested, has been proved. This theorem at once solves the decision problem for the equality formulas. It is sufficient to state the solution for wffs without free variables.

*An equality formula without free variables which is in prenex normal form and has k quantifiers, is universally valid if it is valid in the domains with* 1, 2, ..., *and k elements. It is valid in no domain at all if it is not valid in any of the domains with* 1, 2, ..., *k elements. Generally it is valid in those domains with* 1, 2, ..., *or k elements which may be found out by the decision procedure for domains with a finite number of elements (see* § 2 *of chapter I), and in every other domain, resp. in no other domain, if it is valid resp. not valid in a domain with k elements.*

As an example the reader may take the wff

$$(Ex)(Ey)\overline{x=y}\ \&\ (Ex)(Ey)(Ez)(Eu)(v)(v=x \vee v=y \vee v=z \vee v=u)\ \&$$
$$\&\ (Ex)(Ey)((z)(z=x \vee z=y) \vee (Ez)(Eu)(\overline{x=y}\ \&\ \overline{x=z}\ \&\ \overline{x=u}\ \&\ \overline{y=z}\ \&$$
$$\&\ \overline{y=u}\ \&\ \overline{z=u}))$$

and prove that it is only valid in a domain of two and in a domain of four elements, so that the assertion of the validity of the wff is equivalent to the statement that the domain of individuals has two or four elements.

In special cases, as in that of the last wff, the decision procedure may be abbreviated by using the following theorems:

*E*22. *A wff* $\mathfrak{A}\ \&\ \mathfrak{B}$ *is valid in a domain if* $\mathfrak{A}$ *and* $\mathfrak{B}$ *are valid in that domain, and conversely. A wff* $\mathfrak{A} \vee \mathfrak{B}$ *is valid in a domain if* $\mathfrak{A}$ *or* $\mathfrak{B}$ *is valid in that domain, and conversely, provided that* $\mathfrak{A}$ *and* $\mathfrak{B}$ *have no free variables.*

## 2. Another criterion for the universal validity of equality formulas

We will give another solution of the decision problem for equality formulas, but only for the form I of the problem. If only the universal validity of equality formulas has to be decided, this criterion sometimes reaches the desired result in fewer steps than the previous one. This is independent of the fact that the proof of the validity of the criterion is more complicated. This second method, by the way, does not make use of the valuation in finite domains.

An equality formula without free variables is called *reduced* if it is a conjunction of wffs or a single wff of the following kind. The wffs are in prenex normal form; their prefixes consist only of universal quantifiers; their matrices are in conjunctive normal form and do not contain prime formulas of the form $\mathfrak{a}=\mathfrak{b}$ with different variables $\mathfrak{a}$ and $\mathfrak{b}$ which stand under a negation-bar.

*From every equality formula which is in prenex normal form or which is a conjunction of wffs in prenex normal form we can construct a reduced formula so that the equality formula is universally valid, if and only if the reduced formula is universally valid.*

To avoid misunderstandings this does not mean that the equality formula and its reduced formula are equivalent. E.g. if two wffs are both not universally valid, it is possible that one of them is valid in a certain domain, while the other is not.

We first describe the construction of the reduced formula. This is done in several steps. We start from a conjunction $\mathfrak{A}_1 \mathbin{\&} \dots \mathbin{\&} \mathfrak{A}_k$ of wffs in prenex normal form. We will characterize each $\mathfrak{A}_i$ by a natural number. If $\mathfrak{A}_i$ is reduced, the number is 0. If $\mathfrak{A}_i$ is not reduced but has only universal quantifiers, the number is 1. If $\mathfrak{A}_i$ has $m$ existential quantifiers preceding universal ones and $n$ other existential quantifiers, the number is $2m+n+1$. In such a conjunction, we replace in a certain manner the first conjunction term $\mathfrak{A}_i$, which is not reduced, by a wff $\mathfrak{B}$, or by a conjunction $\mathfrak{B} \mathbin{\&} \mathfrak{C}$ such that the numbers assigned to $\mathfrak{B}$ and $\mathfrak{C}$ are less than the number as signed to $\mathfrak{A}_i$. By repeating such a transformation a finite number of times, $\mathfrak{A}_1 \mathbin{\&} \dots \mathbin{\&} \mathfrak{A}_n$ evidently becomes a reduced formula.

We distinguish several cases.

1) $\mathfrak{A}_i$ has only universal quantifiers.

We bring the matrix of $\mathfrak{A}_i$ into conjunctive normal form. Each conjunction term of the matrix is a disjunction of formulas of the form $\mathfrak{a}=\mathfrak{b}$ or $\overline{\mathfrak{a}=\mathfrak{b}}$, including the case when there is only one such formula. If a conjunction term contains a disjunction term $\overline{\mathfrak{a}=\mathfrak{b}}$ with different variables $\mathfrak{a}$ and $\mathfrak{b}$, we delete $\overline{\mathfrak{a}=\mathfrak{b}}$ and replace $\mathfrak{a}$ by $\mathfrak{b}$

in all occurrences of $\mathfrak{a}$ in the conjunction term. If the conjunction term consists only of $\overline{\mathfrak{a}=\mathfrak{b}}$, we replace it by $\overline{\mathfrak{b}=\mathfrak{b}}$. This is repeated as often as possible, vacuous quantifiers being deleted, until $\mathfrak{A}_i$ is transformed into a reduced formula. The transformation of $\mathfrak{A}_i$ is an equivalence transformation; for by $E8$, $E17$, and $E14$ of II, § 2, $(x)(\overline{x=y} \vee \mathfrak{A}(x, y) \,\&\, \mathfrak{B}(x))$ can be transformed successively into $(x)(\overline{x=y} \vee \mathfrak{A}(x, y)) \,\&\, (x)\mathfrak{B}(x)$, $\mathfrak{A}(y, y) \,\&\, (x)\mathfrak{B}(x)$, $(x)(\mathfrak{A}(y, y) \,\&\, \mathfrak{B}(x))$.

2) The prefix of $\mathfrak{A}_i$ begins with an existential quantifier. We replace the existential quantifier by a universal quantifier for the same variable; the characteristic number of $\mathfrak{A}_i$ is thereby diminished.

3) The prefix of $\mathfrak{A}_i$ begins with a universal quantifier. There are $n$ existential quantifiers, but none of them precedes a universal one. $\mathfrak{A}_i$ has a form

$$(x_1) \ldots (x_p)(Ey_1)(Ey_2) \ldots (Ey_n)\mathfrak{B}(x_1, \ldots, x_p, y_1, y_2, \ldots, y_n)$$

where $\mathfrak{B}$ contains no quantifiers.

We replace this formula by

$$(x_1) \ldots (x_p)(Ey_2) \ldots (Ey_n)(\mathfrak{B}(x_1, \ldots, x_p, x_1, y_2, \ldots, y_n) \vee \\ \vee \mathfrak{B}(x_1, \ldots, x_p, x_2, y_2, \ldots, y_n) \vee \ldots \vee \mathfrak{B}(x_1, \ldots, x_p, x_p, y_2, \ldots, y_n)).$$

4) The prefix of $\mathfrak{A}_i$ begins with a universal quantifier. There are existential quantifiers preceding universal ones. $\mathfrak{A}_i$ has the form $(x_1) \ldots (x_p)(Ey)\mathfrak{B}(x_1, \ldots, x_p, y)$. $\mathfrak{B}$ this time contains quantifiers, some of which are universal quantifiers. We replace $\mathfrak{A}_i$ at first by the conjunction of the two formulas

(i) $$(x_1) \ldots (x_p)(\mathfrak{B}(x_1, \ldots, x_p, x_1) \vee \ldots \vee \mathfrak{B}(x_1, \ldots, x_p, x_p) \vee \\ \vee (Ey)(\overline{y=x_1} \,\&\, \ldots \,\&\, \overline{y=x_p}))$$

and

(ii) $$(x_1) \ldots (x_p)(y)(\mathfrak{B}(x_1, \ldots, x_p, x_1) \vee \ldots \vee \mathfrak{B}(x_1, \ldots, x_p, x_p) \vee \\ \vee \mathfrak{B}(x_1, \ldots, x_p, y) \vee y=x_1 \vee \ldots \vee y=x_p).$$

The wffs (i) and (ii) are not in prenex normal form. After having rewritten the bound variables, we restore the prenex normal forms of (i) and (ii) in the following way. First, the universal quantifiers of the disjunction terms of the form $\mathfrak{B}(x_1, \ldots, x_p, \mathfrak{b})$, which are not preceded in these wffs by existential quantifiers, are placed behind $(x_1) \ldots (x_p)$ resp. $(x_1) \ldots (x_p)(y)$ in the order in which they occur in (i) ((ii)). Then, or at once if no universal quantifiers of the above-mentioned kind exist, the existential quantifiers of the wffs $\mathfrak{B}(x_1, \ldots, x_p, \mathfrak{b})$ now not preceded in these wffs by universal ones, are placed behind the quantifiers already in correct position, but only in the number in which they occur in a single wff $\mathfrak{B}(x_1, \ldots, x_p, \mathfrak{b})$. This can be done by use of the equivalence between

$$(Ez_1)\mathfrak{C}_1(z_1) \vee (Ez_2)\mathfrak{C}_2(z_2) \vee \ldots \vee (Ez_q)\mathfrak{C}_q(z_q) \text{ and } (Ez_1)(\mathfrak{C}_1(z_1) \vee \ldots \vee \mathfrak{C}_q z_1))$$

which is a consequence of $E7$ of III, § 2. With the new wff we repeat the procedure until all the quantifiers of the wffs $\mathfrak{B}(x_1, \ldots, x_p, \mathfrak{b})$ are placed at the beginning of the wff. (ii) is then in prenex normal form. In (i), as a last step, the quantifier $(Ey)$ is placed so as to conclude the prefix. The prenex normal forms of (i) and (ii) have fewer existential quantifiers preceding the universal ones ones than $\mathfrak{A}_i$, while the total number of existential quantifiers has not increased.

As an example we construct the reduced formula of

$$(x)(Ey)(z)(y=x \ \& \ \overline{y=z}).$$

The two formulas (ii) and (i) are here

$$(x)(y)((z)(x=x \ \& \ \overline{x=z}) \vee (z)(y=x \ \& \ \overline{y=z}) \vee y=x)$$

and

$$(x)((z)(x=x \ \& \ \overline{x=z}) \vee (Ey)(\overline{y=x})).$$

Their prenex normal forms are

$$(x)(y)(z)(u)((x=x \ \& \ \overline{x=z}) \vee (y=x \ \& \ \overline{y=u}) \vee y=x)$$

and

$$(x)(z)(Ey)((x=x \ \& \ \overline{x=z}) \vee \overline{y=x}).$$

Bringing the matrix of the first of the last two formulas into conjunctive normal form yields

$$(x)(y)(z)(x=x \vee y=x \ \& \ \overline{x=z} \vee y=x)$$

and

$$*(x)(y)(x=x \vee y=x \;\&\; y=x)$$

as its reduced form. The second of the two formulas is further transformed into

$$(x)(z)(((x=x \;\&\; \overline{x=z}) \vee \overline{x=x}) \vee ((x=x \;\&\; \overline{x=z}) \vee \overline{z=x}))$$

and

$$(x)(z)(\overline{x=z} \vee \overline{x=x} \vee \overline{z=x})$$

if the matrix is brought into conjunctive normal form. The reduced formula of the last wff is $(z)(\overline{z=z} \vee \overline{z=z})$, or $(z)(\overline{z=z})$. The reduced formula of $(x)(Ey)(z)(y=x \;\&\; \overline{y=z})$ is therefore the conjunction of the last formula and of *.

The construction of the reduced formula can be abbreviated by replacing in some wffs a prime formula of the form $\mathfrak{a}=\mathfrak{a}$ by $T$, and by eliminating $T$ after the methods of II, § 3.

For instance, when treating the previous example, the first two formulas (ii) and (i) are

$$(x)(y)((z)(T \;\&\; \overline{x=z}) \vee (z)(y=x \;\&\; \overline{y=z}) \vee y=x)$$

and

$$(x)((z)(T \;\&\; \overline{x=z}) \vee (Ey)\overline{y=x})$$

which by elimination of $T$ become

$(x)(y)((z)\overline{x=z} \vee (z)(y=x \;\&\; \overline{y=z}) \vee y=x)$ and $(x)((z)\overline{x=z} \vee (Ey)\overline{y=x})$.

The two prenex normal forms are

$(x)(y)(z)(u)(\overline{x=z} \vee (y=x \;\&\; \overline{y=u}) \vee y=x)$ and $(x)(z)(Ey)(\overline{x=z} \vee \overline{y=x})$.

The reduced form of the first wff is $(y)(z)(y=z)$. The second wff is transformed again into $(z)(\overline{z=z})$. The reduced formula of $(x)(Ey)(z)(y=x \;\&\; \overline{y=z})$ is now

$$(y)(z)(y=z) \;\&\; (z)(\overline{z=z}).$$

In order to make use of the asserted relation between an equality formula and its reduced formula for the decision problem, we must know the conditions under which a reduced formula is universally valid. A reduced formula $\mathfrak{A}_1 \;\&\; \ldots \;\&\; \mathfrak{A}_k$ is universally valid if each conjunction term is universally valid. A conjunction term such as $\mathfrak{A}_i$ is universally valid, if and only if every conjunction term of its matrix contains a disjunction term of the form $\mathfrak{a}=\mathfrak{a}$. Otherwise, there would be a conjunction term which is a disjunction of terms of the form $\overline{\mathfrak{a}=\mathfrak{a}}$ and $\mathfrak{b}=\mathfrak{c}$ only where $\mathfrak{c}$ and $\mathfrak{b}$ are different variables. If we take a domain in which there are as many elements as different variables in this conjunction term, and if we assign to each variable an element of the domain, but different elements to different variables; then this conjunction term, and consequently the reduced formula, would get the value $F$. On the other hand, it is obvious that $\mathfrak{A}_i$ is universally valid under the above conditions, since $x=x$ is universally valid.

Example: The wff $(x)(Ey)(z)(y=x \mathbin{\&} \overline{y=z})$ is not universally valid, since its reduced formula is not.

Now for the proof of the criterion. We have to show that each transformation 1) through 4) of a wff $\mathfrak{A}_i$ into another wff satisfies the condition that the two formulas are both universally valid, or both not universally valid. For 1) this is clear, since 1) is an equivalence transformation. This is the case too for 2). If the equality formula $(Ex)\mathfrak{A}(x)$, where $\mathfrak{A}(x)$ contains no free variables other than $x$, is true in a domain $D$, there is an element $a$ of $D$ such that $\mathfrak{A}(a)$ is true; $\mathfrak{A}(b)$ is then true for every other element $b$ of $D$ (see the second theorem in § 1 of this chapter). This means that $(x)\mathfrak{A}(x)$ is true in $D$. On the other hand, it is obvious that $(Ex)\mathfrak{A}(x)$ is true in a domain $D$ if $(x)\mathfrak{A}(x)$ is.

The other transformations are no equivalence transformations. $(Ey_2)\dots(Ey_n)(\mathfrak{B}(a_1,\dots,a_p,a_1,y_2,\dots,y_n) \vee \dots \vee \mathfrak{B}(a_1,\dots,a_p,a_p,y_2,\dots,y_n))$ may be true in a domain $D$ for certain elements $a_1, \dots, a_p$ of that domain. There is then an element $b$, namely one of the elements $a_1, \dots, a_p$, such that $(Ey_2) \dots (Ey_n)\mathfrak{B}(a_1, \dots, a_p, b, y_2, \dots, y_n)$, and consequently $(Ey_1)(Ey_2) \dots (Ey_n)\mathfrak{B}(a_1, \dots, a_p, y_1, y_2, \dots, y_n)$, are true in $D$. On the other hand, $(x_1) \dots (x_p)(Ey_1) \dots (Ey_n)\mathfrak{B}(x_1, \dots, x_p, y_1, \dots, y_n)$ may be universally valid. Let $a_1, \dots, a_p$ be an arbitrary set of elements, not necessarily all different, taken from some domain $D$. Since the wff is universally valid, it is valid in the domain consisting only of the elements $a_1, \dots, a_p$. This means that there may be found elements $b_1, \ldots, b_n$ in that domain such that $\mathfrak{B}(a_1, \ldots, a_p, b_1, \ldots, b_n)$ is true in the domain. The last formula is true in any other domain containing the elements $a_1, \ldots, a_p$, for the valuation of this formula depends only upon the relation of equality between $a_1, \ldots, a_p, b_1, \ldots, b_n$. Since $b_1$ is one of the elements $a_1, \ldots, a_p$,

$$\mathfrak{B}(a_1, \ldots, a_p, a_1, b_2, \ldots, b_n) \vee \ldots \vee \mathfrak{B}(a_1, \ldots, a_p, a_p, b_2, \ldots, b_n)$$

and

$$(Ey_2) \ldots (Ey_n)(\mathfrak{B}(a_1, \ldots, a_p, a_1, y_2, \ldots, y_n) \vee \ldots \vee \mathfrak{B}(a_1, \ldots, a_p, a_p, y_2, \ldots, y_n))$$

are true in any such domain. This means that

$$(x_1) \ldots (x_p)(Ey_2) \ldots (Ey_n)(\mathfrak{B}(x_1, \ldots, x_p, x_1, y_2, \ldots, y_n) \vee \ldots \vee \mathfrak{B}(x_1, \ldots, x_p, x_p, y_2, \ldots, y_n))$$

is universally valid.

Let $(x_1) \ldots (x_p)(Ey)\mathfrak{B}(x_1, \ldots, x_p, y)$ be a wff which has the structure described in transformation 4) and which is universally valid. In any domain $D$ containing the elements $a_1, \ldots, a_p$, there is an element $b$ such that $\mathfrak{B}(a_1, \ldots, a_p, b)$ is true. Either $b$ is one of the elements $a_1, \ldots, a_p$ or it is different from all these elements; in the second case, $\mathfrak{B}(a_1, \ldots, a_p, c)$ is true for any element $c$ different from $a_1, \ldots, a_p$ (see the second theorem of § 1 of this chapter). Therefore,

$$(\alpha) \quad \mathfrak{B}(a_1, \ldots, a_p, a_1) \vee \ldots \vee \mathfrak{B}(a_1, \ldots, a_p, a_p) \vee (\overline{b=a_1} \;\&\; \ldots \;\&\; \overline{b=a_p})$$

is true, and

$$(\alpha\alpha) \quad \mathfrak{B}(a_1, \ldots, a_p, a_1) \vee \ldots \vee \mathfrak{B}(a_1, \ldots, a_p, a_p) \vee \mathfrak{B}(a_1, \ldots, a_p, c) \vee c=a_1 \vee \ldots \vee c=a_p$$

is true for an arbitrary $c$. This means that

$$(x_1) \ldots (x_p)(\mathfrak{B}(x_1, \ldots, x_p, x_1) \vee \ldots \vee \mathfrak{B}(x_1, \ldots, x_p, x_p) \vee (Ey)(\overline{y=x_1} \;\&\; \ldots \;\&\; \overline{y=x_p}))$$

and

$$(x_1) \ldots (x_p)(y)(\mathfrak{B}(x_1, \ldots, x_p, x_1) \vee \ldots \vee \mathfrak{B}(x_1, \ldots, x_p, x_p) \vee \mathfrak{B}(x_1, \ldots, x_p, y) \vee y=x_1 \vee \ldots \vee y=x_p)$$

are universally valid.

On the other hand, let the last two wffs be universally valid and further, let $a_1, \ldots, a_p$ be elements of some domain $D$; then there is an element $b$ such that ($\alpha$) is true in $D$, and suchthat ($\alpha\alpha$) is true if in that formula $c$ is replaced by $b$. If $b$ is identical with one of the elements $a_1, \ldots, a_p$, then $\mathfrak{B}(a_1, \ldots, a_p, b)$ is true, since ($\alpha$) is; if $b$ is different from $a_1, \ldots, a_p$, then, since ($\alpha\alpha$) is true, one of the wffs $\mathfrak{B}(a_1, \ldots, a_p, a_1), \ldots, \mathfrak{B}(a_1, \ldots, a_p, a_p), \mathfrak{B}(a_1, \ldots, a_p, b)$ is true. At any rate, $(Ey)\mathfrak{B}(a_1, \ldots, a_p, y)$ is true. This means that $(x_1) \ldots (x_p)(Ey)$ $\mathfrak{B}(x_1, \ldots, x_p, y)$ is universally valid.

Thus, all the transformations 1) through 4) have been shown to have the asserted property.

The argumentation of this § 2 would also show the completeness of any axiomatic system for universally valid equality formulas by which the reduced formulas having this property are deducible and which contains the inverses of the transformation rules 1)—4) as primitive or derived deduction rules.

# IV

# SOLUTION OF THE DECISION PROBLEM FOR WELL-FORMED FORMULAS CONTAINING ONLY MONADIC PREDICATE VARIABLES

In this chapter we consider wffs which have only prime formulas of the form $\mathfrak{a} = \mathfrak{b}$ and $\mathfrak{U}^1\mathfrak{a}$, from which $n$-adic predicate variables are excluded if $n \geqslant 2$. The possibility of decision in this case as well as in the previously treated case of the equality formulas, was first recognized by L. Löwenheim [1]. Simpler proofs have been given by Th. Skolem [1] and by H. Behmann [1]. The method used by all of them consists in transforming a wff into an equivalent one from which the predicate variables have been eliminated. The three authors could make use of the preparatory work of E. Schröder in the first and second volume of his "Algebra der Logik". A representation of the method used by H. Behmann is to be found in D. Hilbert and P. Bernays [1], I, pp. 146ff).

More recent modifications of the methods (see W. V. Quine [1], G. H. von Wright [1], D. Hilbert and W. Ackermann [1], pp. 41—43) treat the more special case in which bound quantifiers for predicate variables and the sign of equality do not occur in the wffs; then the decision method can be simplified. The first mentioned three papers solve the problem in full generality.

## 1. Solution of the form II of the decision problem for wffs which do not contain bound predicate variables and the sign of equality

In the solution given here, use is made of the valuation of a wff in finite domains. The free monadic predicate variables occurring in a given wff may be of the number $k$. We prove the following theorem:

*If the wff is valid in a domain with* $2^k$ *or more elements, it is universally valid.*

We first establish a *lemma*, which will also be used in later sections and the validity of which is not restricted to wffs with only monadic predicate variables.

Let $\mathfrak{A}(x_1, \ldots, x_m, G_1, \ldots, G_k)$ $(m \geqslant 0)$ be a wff without bound predicate variables and without the sign of equality containing the free individual variables $x_1, \ldots, x_m$ and the free predicate variables (not necessarily monadic ones) $G_1, \ldots, G_k$. $D$ and $D'$ may be two domains such that $D$ has a cardinal number which is greater than, or equal to, that of $D'$. An assignment $a_1, \ldots, a_m, \Psi_1, \ldots, \Psi_k$ for the free variables of $\mathfrak{A}$ in $D$ is called an *extension* of an assignment $a_1', \ldots, a_m', \Psi_1', \ldots, \Psi_k'$ in $D'$ provided the following conditions are fulfilled: (1) To every element $b$ of $D$ there corresponds in a unique way an element $b'$ of $D'$, and every element of $D'$ corresponds to some element of $D$. (2) The elements corresponding to $a_1, \ldots, a_m$ are respectively $a_1', \ldots, a_m'$. (3) The ordered pair $(a', b')$ of $D'$ corresponds to the ordered pair $(a, b)$ of $D$ and so forth. (4) For any $i$, $\Psi_i$ is true (false) for an element of $D$ (for an ordered $n$-tuple of elements of $D$) if $\Psi_i'$ is true (false) for the corresponding element (the corresponding $n$-tuple of $D'$).

Our assertion is: $\mathfrak{A}(a_1, \ldots, a_m, \Psi_1, \ldots, \Psi_k)$ is true in $D$, if and only if $\mathfrak{A}(a_1', \ldots, a_m', \Psi_1', \ldots, \Psi_k')$ is true in $D'$.

We prove this by induction on the total number of logical constants and quantifiers occurring in $\mathfrak{A}$. The assertion is evident for prime formulas, since prime formulas of the form $\mathfrak{a} = \mathfrak{b}$ do not occur. Otherwise, $\mathfrak{A}$ has one of the forms $\overline{\mathfrak{B}}$, $\mathfrak{B} \,\&\, \mathfrak{C}$, $\mathfrak{B} \vee \mathfrak{C}$, $(Ey)\mathfrak{B}(y)$ or $(y)\mathfrak{B}(y)$. In the first three cases, the assertion obviously is true for $\mathfrak{A}$ if it holds for $\mathfrak{B}$ ($\mathfrak{B}$ and $\mathfrak{C}$). If $(Ey)\mathfrak{B}(y, a_1, \ldots, a_m, \Psi_1, \ldots, \Psi_k)$ is true in $D$, there is an element $b$ of $D$ such that $\mathfrak{B}(b, a_1, \ldots, a_m, \Psi_1, \ldots, \Psi_k)$ is true; then, as $\mathfrak{B}$ has less quantifiers than $\mathfrak{A}$, $\mathfrak{B}(b', a_1', \ldots, a_m', \Psi_1', \ldots, \Psi_k')$ is true in $D'$, and therefore,

$$(Ey)\mathfrak{B}(y, a_1', \ldots, a_m', \Psi_1', \ldots, \Psi_k')$$

is true. If $(Ey)\mathfrak{B}(y, a_1', \ldots, a_m', \Psi_1', \ldots, \Psi_k')$ is true in $D'$, then there is an element $b'$ of $D'$ such that $\mathfrak{B}(b', a_1', \ldots, a_m', \Psi_1', \ldots, \Psi_k')$ is true. If $b$ is an element of $D$ such that $b'$ corresponds to $b$, $\mathfrak{B}(b, a_1, \ldots, a_m, \Psi_1, \ldots, \Psi_k)$, and therefore, $(Ey)\mathfrak{B}(y, a_1, \ldots, a_m, \Psi_1, \ldots, \Psi_k)$ are true in $D$. If $(y)\mathfrak{B}(y, a_1, \ldots, a_m, \Psi_1, \ldots, \Psi_k)$ is true (false) in $D$, then $(y)\mathfrak{B}(y, a'_1, \ldots, a'_m, \Psi'_1, \ldots, \Psi'_k)$ is true (false) in $D'$, since these two formulas have the same truth-value as the negations of $(Ey)\mathfrak{B}(y, a_1, \ldots, a_m, \Psi_1, \ldots, \Psi_k)$ and $(Ey)\mathfrak{B}(y, a'_1, \ldots, a'_m, \Psi'_1, \ldots, \Psi'_k)$ This completes our induction and the proof of our lemma.

Let $\mathfrak{A}(x_1, \ldots, x_m, G_1, \ldots, G_k)$ have the same meaning as in the lemma except that the predicate variables $G_1, \ldots, G_k$ are all monadic ones. Further, let $D_1$ be a domain with $2^k$ or more elements in which $\mathfrak{A}$ may be valid and let $D_2$ be some other domain in which monadic propositional functions $\Psi_1, \ldots, \Psi_k$ are defined. We divide $D_2$ into several classes. Two elements $a$ and $b$ of $D_2$ are said to belong to the same class if for all $i$, $\Psi_i(a)$ and $\Psi_i(b)$ have the same values; otherwise they belong to different classes. The number of classes of $D_2$ is at most $2^k$. We now construct a subdomain $D_3$ of $D_2$ consisting of just one element of each class. To every element of $D_2$ we let correspond the element of $D_3$ belonging to the same class. We define propositional functions $\Psi'_1, \ldots, \Psi'_k$ in $D_3$ which have the same value for elements of $D_3$ as the functions $\Psi_1, \ldots, \Psi_k$. If $a_1, \ldots, a_m$ are arbitrary elements of $D_2$ and $a'_1, \ldots, a'_m$ the corresponding elements of $D_3$, then the assignment $a_1, \ldots, a_m, \Psi_1, \ldots, \Psi_k$ in $D_2$ is an extension of the assignment $a'_1, \ldots, a'_m, \Psi'_1, \ldots, \Psi'_k$ in $D_3$. According to our lemma, $\mathfrak{A}(a_1, \ldots, a_m, \Psi_1, \ldots, \Psi_k)$ is true in $D_2$ if $\mathfrak{A}(a'_1, \ldots, a'_m, \Psi'_1, \ldots, \Psi'_k)$ is in $D_3$. Since $D_1$ has at least as many elements as $D_3$, we can let an element of $D_3$ correspond in a unique way to each element of $D_1$ and have elements $a''_1, \ldots, a''_m$ of $D_1$ and propositional functions $\Psi''_1, \ldots, \Psi''_k$ over that domain such that $a''_1, \ldots, a''_m, \Psi''_1, \ldots, \Psi''_k$ is an extension of $a'_1, \ldots, a'_m, \Psi'_1, \ldots, \Psi'_k$. Since $\mathfrak{A}(x_1, \ldots, x_m, G_1, \ldots, G_k)$ is valid in $D_1$, $\mathfrak{A}(a''_1, \ldots, a''_m, \Psi''_1, \ldots, \Psi''_k)$ is true in $D_1$. According to our lemma, $\mathfrak{A}(a'_1, \ldots, a'_m, \Psi'_1, \ldots, \Psi'_k)$ is true in $D_3$, and so $\mathfrak{A}(a_1, \ldots, a_m, \Psi_1, \ldots, \Psi_k)$ is true in $D_2$. Because $a_1, \ldots, a_m, \Psi_1, \ldots, \Psi_k$ were arbitrary, $\mathfrak{A}(x_1, \ldots, x_m, G_1, \ldots, G_k)$ is valid in $D_2$, and thus our theorem has been proved.

By the theorem we obtain a decision procedure for the wffs in question. *A wff with $k$ free monadic predicate variables is universally valid if it is valid in a domain with $2^k$ elements. If it is not valid in such a domain, it cannot be valid in a domain with more than $2^k$ elements. In order to obtain in the last case a complete solution of* *the form II of the decision problem, the validity in domains with* 1, 2, ..., $k-1$ *elements has to be determined.*

## 2. Elimination theorems

The solution of the decision problem for wffs with bound predicate variables is obtained, as will be seen in § 3, by eliminating these predicate variables from the wff. The following elimination theorem is sufficient for this purpose.

*E*23. *Let* $\mathfrak{A}(x)$ *and* $\mathfrak{B}(x)$ *be wffs (also with dyadic predicate variables, etc.) not containing the predicate variable G.* $(EG)(x)(\mathfrak{A}(x) \vee Gx \,\&\, \mathfrak{B}(x) \vee \overline{Gx})$ *is then equivalent to* $(x)(\mathfrak{A}(x) \vee \mathfrak{B}(x))$; *likewise,* $(G)(Ex)((\mathfrak{A}(x) \,\&\, Gx) \vee (\mathfrak{B}(x) \,\&\, \overline{Gx}))$ *is equivalent to* $(Ex)(\mathfrak{A}(x) \,\&\, \mathfrak{B}(x))$. *The case when* $\mathfrak{A}$ *or* $\mathfrak{B}$ *do not contain the free variable x is included if vacuous quantifiers are not written.*

Indeed, if $(EG)(x)(\mathfrak{A}(x) \vee Gx \,\&\, \mathfrak{B}(x) \vee \overline{Gx})$ is true in a domain $D$, or if it is true by an assignment for its free variables if such occur, there is a propositional function $\Psi$ such that $\mathfrak{A}(a) \vee \Psi(a) \,\&\, \mathfrak{B}(a) \vee \overline{\Psi(a)}$ is true for every element $a$ of the domain by the given assignment. Because $\Psi(a)$ and $\overline{\Psi(a)}$ cannot both be true, $\mathfrak{A}(a)$ or $\mathfrak{B}(a)$, i.e. $\mathfrak{A}(a) \vee \mathfrak{B}(a)$ is true. Since $a$ was arbitrary, $(x)(\mathfrak{A}(x) \vee \mathfrak{B}(x))$ is true by the given assignment. If the last formula is true in $D$ by an assignment for its free variables, we define a propositional function $\Psi$ relative to this assignment such that for every $a$ of $D$, $\Psi(a)$ is true only if $\mathfrak{B}(a)$ is true by the assignment; then $(x)(\mathfrak{A}(x) \vee \Psi(x) \,\&\, \mathfrak{B}(x) \vee \overline{\Psi(x)})$ is true by the assignment and so is $(EG)(x)(\mathfrak{A}(x) \vee Gx \,\&\, \mathfrak{B}(x) \vee \overline{Gx})$. The second equivalence is a consequence of the first one; $\overline{(G)(Ex)((\mathfrak{A}(x) \,\&\, Gx) \vee (\mathfrak{B}(x) \,\&\, \overline{Gx}))}$ can be given the equivalent form $\overline{(EG)(x)(\overline{\mathfrak{A}(x)} \vee \overline{Gx} \,\&\, \overline{\mathfrak{B}(x)} \vee Gx)}$ which is equivalent again to $(x)(\overline{\mathfrak{A}(x)} \vee \overline{\mathfrak{B}(x)})$ and to $\overline{(Ex)(\mathfrak{A}(x) \,\&\, \mathfrak{B}(x))}$.

Similar theorems not needed for the solution of the decision problem treated in this chapter may be stated for dyadic, triadic, ... predicate variables such as, for instance, a theorem about the equivalence between $(EG)(x)(y)(\mathfrak{A}(x, y) \vee Gxy \,\&\, \mathfrak{B}(x, y) \vee \overline{Gxy})$ and $(x)(y)(\mathfrak{A}(x, y) \vee \mathfrak{B}(x, y))$, or between $(G)(Ex)(Ey)((\mathfrak{A}(x, y) \,\&\, Gxy) \vee (\mathfrak{B}(x, y) \,\&\, \overline{Gxy}))$ and $(Ex)(Ey)(\mathfrak{A}(x, y) \,\&\, \mathfrak{B}(x, y))$. The proof is similar to that of *E*23.

Setting aside the actual purpose of this chapter, elimination theorems may be generally of some use. Besides giving the solution of the decision problem in certain special cases they may also sometimes simplify a wff so that the solution of the decision problem, to be obtained by other methods, is more easily reached. Studies on the elimination problem are to be found in the third volume of Schröder's "Algebra der Logik" and with W. Ackermann [2, 3]. We mention only the following theorems taken from the last cited paper, which are a generalisation of *E*23 and the corresponding theorems for dyadic, etc. predicate variables.

*E*24. *$\mathfrak{A}(x, Gx)$ may be a wff with the free individual variable $x$, the free monadic predicate variable $G$ and possibly other free variables. The prime formulas of $\mathfrak{A}$ containing $G$ may be all of the form $Gx$. $(EG)(x)\mathfrak{A}(x, Gx)$ is then equivalent to*

$$(x)(EY)\mathfrak{A}(x, Y), \textit{ and } (G)(Ex)\mathfrak{A}(x, Gx)$$

*is equivalent to $(Ex)(Y)\mathfrak{A}(x, Y)$, where $Y$ is a propositional variable.*

*E*23 is a consequence of *E*24. For $(EG)(x)(\mathfrak{A}(x) \vee Gx \,\&\, \mathfrak{B}(x) \vee \overline{Gx})$ may be replaced by $(x)(EY)(\mathfrak{A}(x) \vee Y \,\&\, \mathfrak{B}(x) \vee \overline{Y})$, which according to II, § 3 may be replaced by the equivalent *S*-formula

$$(x)((\mathfrak{A}(x) \vee T \,\&\, \mathfrak{B}(x) \vee \overline{T}) \vee (\mathfrak{A}(x) \vee F \,\&\, \mathfrak{B}(x) \vee \overline{F})).$$

The last formula reduces to $(x)(\mathfrak{B}(x) \vee \mathfrak{A}(x))$.

For the proof we may replace $(x)(EY)\mathfrak{A}(x, Y)$ by the equivalent *S*-formula $(x)(\mathfrak{A}(x, T) \vee \mathfrak{A}(x, F))$. If $\Psi$ is a propositional function in a domain $D$ which is true (false) by a given assignment for any element $a$ of this domain provided that $\mathfrak{A}(a, T)$ respectively $\overline{\mathfrak{A}(a, T) \,\&\, (\mathfrak{A}(a, F))}$ is true, then $\mathfrak{A}(a, T) \vee \mathfrak{A}(a, F)$ and $\mathfrak{A}(a, \Psi(a))$ have the same value for any $a$ by the given assignment. From this the equivalence is immediately derived.

*E*25. *Let $\mathfrak{A}_\mathfrak{y}(x, Gx\mathfrak{y})$ be a wff with the free variables $x$ and $G$ and possibly other free variables. Let the prime formulas of $\mathfrak{A}$ containing $G$ be all of the form $Gx\mathfrak{a}$, where $\mathfrak{a}$ is or is not identical with $x$. Let $\mathfrak{A}_\mathfrak{y}(x, H\mathfrak{y})$ be the wff resulting from the previous one by replacing each prime formula $Gx\mathfrak{a}$ by $H\mathfrak{a}$. $H$ does not occur in $\mathfrak{A}_\mathfrak{y}(x, Gx\mathfrak{y})$. Under these conditions $(EG)(x)\mathfrak{A}_\mathfrak{y}(x, Gx\mathfrak{y})$ and $(x)(EH)\mathfrak{A}_\mathfrak{y}(x, H\mathfrak{y})$, as well as*

*$(G)(Ex)\mathfrak{A}_y(x, Gxy)$ and $(Ex)(H)\mathfrak{A}_y(x, Hy)$, are equivalent wffs. An analogous theorem holds for wffs $\mathfrak{A}_y(x, Gyx)$.*

By application of this theorem a bound dyadic predicate variable is changed to a monadic one. Similar theorems concern the replacement of a bound triadic predicate variable by a dyadic predicate variable, and so forth.

If $(EG)(x)\mathfrak{A}_y(x, Gxy)$ is true by an assignment in a domain $D$, then there is a dyadic propositional function $\Psi$ such that for any $a$, $\mathfrak{A}_y(a, \Psi(a, y))$ is true by this assignment. For any $a$, there is a monadic propositional function $\Phi_a$ for which $\Phi_a(b)$ has the same value as $\Psi(a, b)$ for any $b$. $\mathfrak{A}_y(a, \Phi_a(y))$ is true by the given assignment; this may be proved by induction on the structure of the wff. Therefore, $(EH)\mathfrak{A}_y(a, Hy)$ is true for any $a$. This means that $(x)(EH)\mathfrak{A}_y(x, Hy)$ is true by the assignment. On the other hand, let $(x)(EH)\mathfrak{A}_y(x, Hy)$ be true by some assignment; for every $a$, there is then a monadic propositional function $\Gamma$ such that $\mathfrak{A}_y(a, \Gamma y)$ is true. We select one such $\Gamma$ for each $a$, which we shall designate by $\Phi_a$. Let $\Psi$ be the dyadic propositional function such that for any $a$ and $b$, $\Phi_a(b)$ and $\Psi(a, b)$ have the same value. Since $\mathfrak{A}_y(a, \Phi_a(y))$ is true for any $a$, so is $\mathfrak{A}_y(a, \Psi(a, y))$, which can be demonstrated in a simple manner by induction on the structure of $\mathfrak{A}$. This proves that $(EG)(x)\mathfrak{A}_y(x, Gxy)$ is true by the given assignment.

We illustrate the elimination of monadic predicate variables by carrying it out with the help of the wff

$$(x)(EG)((Ey)(\overline{x=y} \mathbin{\&} Gy) \mathbin{\&} (Ez)(u)(\overline{x=z} \mathbin{\&} \overline{z=u} \vee \overline{Gu})).$$

We place $(Ey)$ and $(Ez)$ at the beginning and change the succession of $(EG)$, $(Ey)$ and $(Ez)$. The formula

$$(x)(Ey)(Ez)(EG)(\overline{x=y} \mathbin{\&} Gy \mathbin{\&} (u)(\overline{x=z} \mathbin{\&} \overline{z=u} \vee \overline{Gu}))$$

is equivalent to $(x)(Ey)(Ez)(EG)(\overline{x=y} \mathbin{\&} Gy \mathbin{\&} \overline{x=z} \mathbin{\&} \overline{Gz})$ by $E14$ and $E17$ of II, § 2. By $E19$ and $E10$ we may write

$$(x)(Ey)(Ez)(\overline{x=y} \mathbin{\&} \overline{x=z} \mathbin{\&} (EG)(Gy \mathbin{\&} \overline{Gz})).$$

$(EG)(Gy \mathbin{\&} \overline{Gz})$ is replaced by $(EG)(u)(\overline{u=y} \vee Gu \mathbin{\&} \overline{u=z} \vee \overline{Gu})$ according to $E17$. By $E23$, this is equivalent to $(u)(\overline{u=y} \vee \overline{u=z})$

which, by making use of $E17$, may be simplified to $\overline{y=z}$. The equality formula $(x)(Ey)(Ez)(\overline{x=y} \;\&\; \overline{x=z} \;\&\; \overline{y=z})$ is therefore equivalent to the wff from which we started.

We give another example for the reduction of a dyadic predicate variable to a monadic one. The wff

$$\begin{gathered}(G)(EH)((x)(Ey)(z)(\overline{x=y} \vee Gx \;\&\; y=z \vee \overline{Gx} \;\&\; Hxz) \;\& \\ \&\; (u)(Ev)(w)(\overline{u=v} \vee \overline{Gv} \;\&\; v=w \vee Gv \vee \overline{Huw}))\end{gathered}$$

is equivalent to

$$\begin{gathered}(G)(EH)(x)((Ey)(z)(\overline{x=y} \vee Gx \;\&\; y=z \vee \overline{Gx} \;\&\; Hxz) \;\& \\ \&\; (Ev)(w)(\overline{x=v} \vee \overline{Gv} \;\&\; v=w \vee Gv \vee \overline{Hxw})),\end{gathered}$$

according to $E8$ of II, § 2. Applying $E25$ we get

$$\begin{gathered}(G)(x)(EH)((Ey)(z)(\overline{x=y} \vee Gx \;\&\; y=z \vee \overline{Gx} \;\&\; Hz) \;\& \\ \&\; (Ev)(w)(\overline{x=v} \vee \overline{Gv} \;\&\; v=w \vee Gv \vee \overline{Hw})).\end{gathered}$$

There is a case in which an arbitrary bound predicate variable may be eliminated and not only replaced by another such variable.

$E26$. *Let $\mathfrak{A}(G)$ be a wff which contains the free predicate variable $G$, but no bound variables at all. We can produce wffs which are equivalent to $(EG)\mathfrak{A}(G)$ and to $(G)\mathfrak{A}(G)$ and which contain no bound variables. If $\mathfrak{A}(G)$ contains only existential (universal quantifiers) which do not stand under a negation-bar, $(EG)\mathfrak{A}(G)$ and $(G)\mathfrak{A}(G)$ are equivalent to a wff from which the bound variable $G$ is eliminated.*

The second part of the assertion is included in the first part, for the quantifiers of $\mathfrak{A}(G)$ may be placed outside the scope of $(EG)((G))$. It is irrelevant for the theorem whether $G$ is a monadic, triadic, ... variable.

It will be sufficient to show this for a dyadic predicate variable, since the procedure in the other cases is analogous. We bring $\mathfrak{A}(G)$ into the disjunctive normal form $\mathfrak{A}_1(G) \vee \ldots \vee \mathfrak{A}_k(G)$. By $E7$ of II, § 2 $(EG)\mathfrak{A}(G)$ is equivalent to $(EG)\mathfrak{A}_1(G) \vee \ldots \vee (EG)\mathfrak{A}_k(G)$. Each conjunction term of a $\mathfrak{A}_i(G)$ containing $G$ has the form $G\mathfrak{a}\mathfrak{b}$ or $\overline{G\mathfrak{a}\mathfrak{b}}$. By using $E19$ and by contracting the scope of $(EG)$ in a wff $(EG)\mathfrak{A}_i(G)$ according to $E9$ and $E10$ so as to exclude all conjunction terms not containing $G$, the scope of $(EG)$ receives the form

$$G\mathfrak{a}_1 \mathfrak{b}_1 \,\&\, \ldots \,\&\, G\mathfrak{a}_m \mathfrak{b}_m \,\&\, \overline{G\mathfrak{c}_1 \mathfrak{d}_1} \,\&\, \ldots \,\&\, \overline{G\mathfrak{c}_n \mathfrak{d}_n}.$$

By applying $E17$ of II, § 2, we may write

$$(EG)(x)(y)(\overline{x=\mathfrak{a}_1} \vee \overline{y=\mathfrak{b}_1} \vee Gxy \,\&\, \ldots \,\&\, \overline{x=\mathfrak{a}_m} \vee \overline{y=\mathfrak{b}_m} \vee Gxy \,\&$$
$$\&\, \overline{x=\mathfrak{c}_1} \vee \overline{y=\mathfrak{d}_1} \vee \overline{Gxy} \,\&\, \ldots \,\&\, \overline{x=\mathfrak{c}_n} \vee \overline{y=\mathfrak{d}_n} \vee \overline{Gxy}),$$

provided that $x$ and $y$ are not among the variables $\mathfrak{a}_1, \ldots, \mathfrak{d}_n$. According to $E21$, the last wff is equivalent to

$$(EG)(x)(y)(\overline{x=\mathfrak{a}_1} \vee \overline{y=\mathfrak{b}_1} \,\&\, \ldots \,\&\, \overline{x=\mathfrak{a}_m} \vee \overline{y=\mathfrak{b}_m}) \vee Gxy \,\&$$
$$\&\, (\overline{x=\mathfrak{c}_1} \vee \overline{y=\mathfrak{d}_1} \,\&\, \ldots \,\&\, \overline{x=\mathfrak{c}_n} \vee \overline{y=\mathfrak{d}_n}) \vee \overline{Gxy})$$

which again according to $E23$, is equivalent to

$$(x)(y)(\overline{x=\mathfrak{a}_1} \vee \overline{y=\mathfrak{b}_1} \,\&\, \ldots \,\&\, \overline{x=\mathfrak{a}_m} \vee \overline{y=\mathfrak{b}_m}) \vee (\overline{x=\mathfrak{c}_1} \vee \overline{y=\mathfrak{d}_1} \,\&$$
$$\&\, \ldots \,\&\, \overline{x=\mathfrak{c}_n} \vee \overline{y=\mathfrak{d}_n})$$

In the last wff the individual quantifiers $(x)$ and $(y)$ can be eliminated by $E17$ after the matrix of the wff has been brought into conjunctive normal form.

The elimination of $(G)$ in $(G)\mathfrak{A}(G)$ is a consequence of the elimination of $(EG)$, for $(G)\mathfrak{A}(G)$ is equivalent to $\overline{(EG)\overline{\mathfrak{A}(G)}}$.

## 3. General solution of the decision problem for wffs with only monadic predicate variables

The general solution of the decision problem for the wffs dealt with in this chapter is obtained by transforming a wff which we can suppose to contain only bound predicate variables into an equivalent equality formula. In our exposition we follow Behmann and partly, Hilbert and Bernays.

Subsequently we shall have to do with wffs

$$(Ex)\mathfrak{A}(x),\ (Ex)(Ey)(\overline{x=y} \,\&\, \mathfrak{A}(x) \,\&\, \mathfrak{A}(y)),$$
$$(Ex)(Ey)(Ez)(\overline{x=y} \,\&\, \overline{x=z} \,\&\, \overline{y=z} \,\&\, \mathfrak{A}(x) \,\&\, \mathfrak{A}(y) \,\&\, \mathfrak{A}(z)), \ldots$$

(with wffs $(x)\mathfrak{A}(x)$, $(Ey)(x)(x=y \vee \mathfrak{A}(x))$,

$$(Ey)(Ez)(x)(x=y \vee x=z \vee \mathfrak{A}(x)), \ldots).$$

For these wffs, we use the abbreviations

$$(E_1x)\mathfrak{A}(x),\ (E_2x)\mathfrak{A}(x),\ (E_3x)\mathfrak{A}(x),\ \ldots,\ (({}_1x)\mathfrak{A}(x),\ ({}_2x)\mathfrak{A}(x),\ ({}_3x)\mathfrak{A}(x),\ \ldots,)$$

which were introduced by Hilbert and Bernays. Generally, $(E_mx)\mathfrak{A}(x)$ is a wff with the prefix $(Ex_1)\ldots(Ex_m)$, whose matrix is the conjunction of all terms $\overline{x_i=x_k}$ $(i<k)$ and of all terms $\mathfrak{A}(x_1), \ldots, \mathfrak{A}(x_m)$. $(x_{m+1})\mathfrak{A}(x)$ has the prefix $(Ex_1)\ldots(Ex_m)(y)$; the matrix is the disjunction of $\mathfrak{A}(y)$ and of all terms $y=x_i$. The abbreviations $(E_mx)\mathfrak{A}(x)$ and $({}_mx)\mathfrak{A}(x)$ are used also for wffs resulting from the wffs above by rewriting the variables or by changing the succession of the conjunction (disjunction) terms or by replacing the terms $\overline{\mathfrak{a}=\mathfrak{b}}$ or $\mathfrak{a}=\mathfrak{b}$ by $\overline{\mathfrak{b}=\mathfrak{a}}$ or $\mathfrak{b}=\mathfrak{a}$. $(E_mx)\mathfrak{A}(x)$ is true by an assignment in a domain, if and only if there are at least $m$ different elements $a_1, \ldots, a_m$ of that domain such that $\mathfrak{A}(a_1), \ldots, \mathfrak{A}(a_m)$ are all true. $({}_mx)\mathfrak{A}(x)$ is true by an assignment, if and only if there are at most $m-1$ different elements $a_1, \ldots, a_{m-1}$ in the domain such that $\mathfrak{A}(a_1), \ldots, \mathfrak{A}(a_{m-1})$ are all false. Therefore, $\overline{({}_mx)\mathfrak{A}(x)}$ and $(E_mx)\overline{\mathfrak{A}(x)}$ as well as $\overline{(E_mx)\mathfrak{A}(x)}$ and $({}_mx)\overline{\mathfrak{A}(x)}$ are equivalent wffs.

We prove three lemmas.

Lemma 1. $\mathfrak{A}(x)$ may be a wff with the free variable $x$, but without the variables $y_1, \ldots, y_k$ and without any bound variable. $(E_mx)(\mathfrak{A}(x) \mathbin{\&} \overline{x=y_1} \mathbin{\&} \ldots \mathbin{\&} \overline{x=y_k})$ can be transformed into an equivalent wff which has only existential quantifiers and in which the variables $y_1, \ldots, y_k$ do not occur in the scopes of quantifiers. The existential quantifiers do not stand under a negation-bar. The new wff has no free variables other than the first one.

The lemma is proved by induction on $k$. If $k$ is 0, the wff already has the desired form. The reduction of $k+1$ to $k$ is achieved by use of the equivalence between

$$(E_mx)(\mathfrak{A}(x) \mathbin{\&} \overline{x=y_1} \mathbin{\&} \ldots \mathbin{\&} \overline{x=y_{k+1}})$$

and

$$(E_{m+1}x)(\mathfrak{A}(x) \mathbin{\&} \overline{x=y_1} \mathbin{\&} \ldots \mathbin{\&} \overline{x=y_k}) \vee (\overline{\mathfrak{A}(y_{k+1})} \mathbin{\&} (E_mx)(\mathfrak{A}(x) \mathbin{\&} \\ \mathbin{\&} \overline{x=y_1} \mathbin{\&} \ldots \mathbin{\&} \overline{x=y_k})).$$

The two wffs are recognized as equivalent in the following way. If there are at least $m$ different elements $a$ of a domain $D$ for which

$\mathfrak{A}(a)$ is true and which are all different from certain elements $b_1, \dots, b_{k+1}$, then $\mathfrak{A}(b_{k+1})$ is either true or false; in the first case, there are $m+1$ elements for which $\mathfrak{A}$ is true and which are different from $b_1, \dots, b_k$; in the second case, $\mathfrak{A}(b_{k+1})$ is false and there are of course still $m$ different elements and these elements are different also from $b_1, \dots, b_k$, for which $\mathfrak{A}$ is true. On the other hand, if $(E_{m+1})(\mathfrak{A}(x)\ \&$ $\&\ \overline{x=y_1}\ \&\ \dots\ \&\ \overline{x=y_k})$ is true by an assignment, $m$ of the $m+1$ elements for which $\mathfrak{A}$ is true must be different from the elements assigned to $y_{k+1}$. If $\overline{\mathfrak{A}(y_{k+1})}\ \&\ (E_m x)(\mathfrak{A}(x)\ \&\ \overline{x=y_1}\ \&\ \dots\ \&\ \overline{x=y_k})$ is true by an assignment, the element assigned to $y_{k+1}$ is different from all the elements for which $\mathfrak{A}$ is true, since $\mathfrak{A}(a)$ and $\overline{\mathfrak{A}(a)}$ cannot both be true for the same $a$.

Lemma 2. Let $\mathfrak{A}(x), y_1, \dots, y_k$ have the same meaning as with lemma 1; then $({}_m x)(\mathfrak{A}(x) \vee x=y_1 \vee \dots \vee x=y_k)$ can be transformed into an equivalent wff in which the variables $y_1, \dots, y_k$ do not appear in the scope of a quantifier and in which the quantifiers appear only in groups of the form $(E\mathfrak{a}_1) \dots (E\mathfrak{a}_n)(\mathfrak{b})$, the scopes of $(E\mathfrak{a}_1), \dots, (E\mathfrak{a}_n), (\mathfrak{b})$ extending to the same point in the formula. Further, no quantifier stands under a negation-bar and the new wff has no free variables other than those which appear free in the old wff. The scopes of the different groups of quantifiers do not overlap.

This is again proved by induction on $k$. The reduction of the case for $k+1$ to that for $k$ is accomplished by making use of the equivalence between

$$({}_m x)(\mathfrak{A}(x) \vee x=y_1 \vee \dots \vee x=y_{k+1})$$

and

$$({}_{m+1} x)(\mathfrak{A}(x) \vee x=y_1 \vee \dots \vee x=y_k)\ \&\ \overline{\mathfrak{A}(y_{k+1})} \vee ({}_m x)(\mathfrak{A}(x) \vee$$
$$\vee\ x=y_1 \vee \dots \vee x=y_k).$$

This equivalence is a consequence of that used in the proof of lemma 1; for if we take the negations of the two wffs and observe that $\overline{({}_m x)\mathfrak{A}(x)}$, $\overline{\mathfrak{A}\ \&\ \mathfrak{B}}$, $\overline{\mathfrak{A} \vee \mathfrak{B}}$, and $\overline{\overline{\mathfrak{A}}}$ are respectively equivalent to $(E_m x)\overline{\mathfrak{A}(x)}$, $\overline{\mathfrak{A}} \vee \overline{\mathfrak{B}}$, $\overline{\mathfrak{A}}\ \&\ \overline{\mathfrak{B}}$ and $\mathfrak{A}$, the equivalence becomes that of lemma 1 if $\overline{\mathfrak{A}(x)}$ is substituted for $\mathfrak{A}(x)$.

In the following, the two lemmas are used only for $m=1$, but for the proof it is necessary to state them for an arbitrary $m$.

Lemma 3. For any wff without bound predicate variables we can construct an equivalent wff having the following properties: (1) All existential quantifiers are placed at the beginning of the formula with scopes extending to the end of the formula. (2) The scope of each universal quantifier is a disjunction of negated or non-negated prime formulas and does not contain free individual variables except that of the quantifier. (3) No quantifier stands under a negation-bar. (The case that there are no universal or no existential quantifiers is included.)

Let $\mathfrak{A}$ be a wff in which the negation-bar stands only over prime formulas and which contains no bound predicate variables. There may be quantifiers initially placed in $\mathfrak{A}$ with scopes extending to the end of the formula. Let $p$ be the number of these quantifiers, provided we do not count the existential quantifiers which are preceeded by no universal quantifier. To have a short expression we will call these $p$ quantifiers the *essential* quantifiers. Besides these initially placed quantifiers, there are only universal quantifiers the scopes of which have the structure described in the lemma.

If the number $p$ is one or greater, we shall construct an equivalent wff of the same character for which $p$ is less. This construction suffices to prove the lemma. For any wff can be given a prenex normal form with the properties of $\mathfrak{A}$.

We distinguish two cases.

1) The last of the essential quantifiers is an existential one. Let $(Ex)$ be this quantifier and $\mathfrak{B}(x)$ its scope. We bring $\mathfrak{B}(x)$ into a disjunctive normal form

$$\mathfrak{B}_1(x) \vee \ldots \vee \mathfrak{B}_n(x) \vee \mathfrak{D}_1 \vee \ldots \vee \mathfrak{D}_q,$$

where the wffs $\mathfrak{D}_i$ may not contain the variable $x$. We transform $(Ex)\mathfrak{B}(x)$ into the equivalent form

$$(Ex)\mathfrak{B}_1(x) \vee \ldots \vee (Ex)\mathfrak{B}_n(x) \vee \mathfrak{D}_1 \vee \ldots \vee \mathfrak{D}_q.$$

Each $\mathfrak{B}_i(x)$ is a conjunction of formulas of the forms $\mathfrak{b}=\mathfrak{c}$, $\overline{\mathfrak{b}=\mathfrak{c}}$, $\mathfrak{U}^1\mathfrak{b}$, $\overline{\mathfrak{U}^1\mathfrak{b}}$, $(\mathfrak{c})\mathfrak{D}(\mathfrak{c})$. The variables $\mathfrak{b}$ and $\mathfrak{c}$ may, or may not, be the same as $x$. We now contract, if possible, the scope of $(Ex)$ in each $(Ex)\mathfrak{B}_i(x)$ by excluding from it all conjunction terms not containing the variable $x$. This can be done by changing the succession of the conjunction terms and by use of the equivalences $E9$ and $E10$ of II, § 2. No conjunction term with universal quantifiers then occurs in the scope of $(Ex)$, for these terms were supposed not to contain the variable $x$. $\mathfrak{C}_i(x)$ may be the new scope of $(Ex)$. If $\mathfrak{C}_i(x)$ has a conjunction term of the form $x=\mathfrak{b}$ or $\mathfrak{b}=x$, where $\mathfrak{b}$ is different from $x$, we then replace $(Ex)\mathfrak{C}_i(x)$ by $\mathfrak{C}_i(\mathfrak{b})$ according to $E18$ of II, § 2, and the transformation of $(Ex)\mathfrak{C}_i(x)$ is finished. If this is not the case, $(Ex)\mathfrak{C}_i(x)$ has a form $(Ex)(\overline{x=\mathfrak{b}_1} \;\&\; \ldots \;\&\; \overline{x=\mathfrak{b}_m} \;\&\; \mathfrak{E}(x))$ $(m \geqslant 0)$, where $\mathfrak{b}_1, \ldots, \mathfrak{b}_m$ are variables belonging to the left $p-1$ essential quantifiers and where $\mathfrak{E}(x)$ is free from such variables. If $m \geqslant 1$, we replace $(Ex)\mathfrak{C}_i(x)$ according to lemma 1 by a wff with only existential quantifiers not standing under a negation-bar, the variables $\mathfrak{b}_1, \ldots, \mathfrak{b}_m$ not appearing in the scope of a quantifier.

After this transformation has been effected with each $(Ex)\mathfrak{C}_i(x)$ and after rewriting bound variables, we place all the existential quantifiers occurring in the transformed formulas $(Ex)\mathfrak{C}_i(x)$ immediately before the left essential quantifiers in $\mathfrak{A}$, extending their scopes to the end of the formula. The new wff has fewer essential quantifiers.

2) Let the last of the essential quantifiers be $(x)$ with the scope $\mathfrak{B}(x)$.

We proceed in a similar way. We bring $\mathfrak{B}(x)$ into a conjunctive normal form

$$\mathfrak{B}_1(x) \;\&\; \ldots \;\&\; \mathfrak{B}_n(x) \;\&\; \mathfrak{D}_1 \;\&\; \ldots \;\&\; \mathfrak{D}_p$$

and write

$$(x)\mathfrak{B}_1(x) \;\&\; \ldots \;\&\; (x)\mathfrak{B}_n(x) \;\&\; \mathfrak{D}_1 \;\&\; \ldots \;\&\; \mathfrak{D}_p$$

instead of $(x)\mathfrak{B}(x)$. In a formula $(x)\mathfrak{B}_i(x)$ we contract the scope of $(x)$ so as to exclude any disjunction term not containing the variable $x$. Let $\mathfrak{C}_i(x)$ be the new scope of $(x)$. If $\mathfrak{C}_i(x)$ has a disjunction term of the form $\overline{x=\mathfrak{b}}$ or $\overline{\mathfrak{b}=x}$ where $\mathfrak{b}$ is a variable different from $x$, we replace $(x)\mathfrak{C}_i(x)$ by $\mathfrak{C}_i(\mathfrak{b})$ according to $E17$ of II, § 2; otherwise, $(x)\mathfrak{C}_i(x)$ is of the form

$$(x)(x=\mathfrak{b}_1 \vee \ldots \vee x=\mathfrak{b}_n \vee \mathfrak{D}(x)) \;\; (m \geqslant 0),$$

where $\mathfrak{D}(x)$ contains no free individual variables besides $x$. If $m \geqslant 1$, we replace $(x)\mathfrak{C}_i(x)$ according to lemma 2. We then put all the existential quantifiers of the transformed wffs $(x)\mathfrak{C}_i(x)$ before the essential quantifiers of $\mathfrak{A}$ after having rewritten the bound variables. The universal quantifiers appear now as they did at first in $\mathfrak{A}$. Thus again $\mathfrak{A}$ is reduced to an equivalent wff of the same character with fewer essential quantifiers.

By applying this reduction $p$ times, $\mathfrak{A}$ is transformed into a wff as described in the lemma.

We now point out how to eliminate the bound predicate variables from a given wff.

Let $(EG)\mathfrak{A}(G)$ be a part of the wff such that $\mathfrak{A}(G)$ contains no bound predicate variables. We give $\mathfrak{A}(G)$ the form mentioned in lemma 3. Let $(Ex_1) \ldots (Ex_m)\mathfrak{B}(G, x_1, \ldots, x_n)$ be this form. In $(EG)(Ex_1) \ldots (Ex_m)\mathfrak{B}(G, x_1 \ldots, x_m)$, the quantifier $(EG)$ can be placed behind $(Ex_1) \ldots (Ex_m)$; then $\mathfrak{B}(G, x_1, \ldots, x_m)$ is brought into disjunctive normal form and the quantifier $(EG)$ is placed before each of these disjunction terms if they contain $G$. This is done by applying $E7$, $E11$, $E12$ of II, § 2. The scope of each $(EG)$ is contracted so as to exclude all component parts not containing $G$. Let $\mathfrak{C}(G)$ be such a contracted scope.

$\mathfrak{C}(G)$ is a conjunction of terms of the form $G\mathfrak{a}$, $\overline{G\mathfrak{b}}$, $(\mathfrak{c})(\mathfrak{A}(\mathfrak{c}) \vee G\mathfrak{c})$ and $(\mathfrak{c})(\mathfrak{B}(\mathfrak{c}) \vee \overline{G\mathfrak{c}})$, where $\mathfrak{A}(\mathfrak{c})$ and $\mathfrak{B}(\mathfrak{c})$ do not contain $G$. The terms $G\mathfrak{a}$ and $\overline{G\mathfrak{b}}$ are replaced by $(\mathfrak{c})(\overline{\mathfrak{c}=\mathfrak{a}} \vee G\mathfrak{c})$ (or by $(\mathfrak{c})(\overline{\mathfrak{c}=\mathfrak{b}} \vee \overline{G\mathfrak{c}})$). By applying $E8$ of II, § 2, $(EG)\mathfrak{C}(G)$ is transformed into a wff $(EG)(\mathfrak{c})\mathfrak{D}(\mathfrak{c}, G\mathfrak{c})$ where $G$ occurs only in prime formulas of the form $G\mathfrak{c}$. By $E23$ of § 2 of this chapter, $(EG)(\mathfrak{c})\mathfrak{D}(\mathfrak{c}, G\mathfrak{c})$ is equivalent to $(\mathfrak{c})(EX)\mathfrak{D}(\mathfrak{c}, X)$. From the last wff, the propositional quantifier can be eliminated according to II, § 3. This procedure is followed wherever $(EG)$ appears. $(EG)\mathfrak{B}(G, x_1, \ldots, x_m)$ is thus transformed into a wff $\mathfrak{C}(x_1, \ldots, x_m)$ without bound predicate variables. $(EG)\mathfrak{A}(G)$ is equivalent to $(Ex_1) \ldots (Ex_m)\mathfrak{C}(x_1, \ldots, x_m)$.

If we have a part $(G)\mathfrak{A}(G)$ of the wff without bound predicate variables other than $G$, then this is replaced by the equivalent wff $\overline{(EG)\overline{\mathfrak{A}(G)}}$ and the $G$ in $(EG)\overline{\mathfrak{A}(G)}$ is eliminated in the above described way.

By this method, the bound predicate variables of a wff can be eliminated successively until none is left. If the wff contains no free predicate variables, the result of the elimination is an equality formula. We therefore may state the theorem:

*Any wff with bound monadic predicate variables but without any other predicate variable can be transformed into an equivalent equality formula.*

As the decision problem in the form II is solved for equality formulas, this holds too for the wffs considered in this chapter.

Taking into consideration how the decision problem was solved for equality formulas, we see that the following statement holds not only for the special class of wffs treated in § 1 of this chapter, but also for any wffs containing only monadic predicate variables.

*Any wff with only monadic predicate variables is either universally valid, or not valid in any domain, or valid only in a finite number of domains with a finite number of individuals, or valid in any domain with the exception of a finite number of finite domains.*

# V

# SOME GENERAL THEOREMS ABOUT THE VALIDITY OF FORMULAS OF THE PREDICATE CALCULUS OF FIRST ORDER INCLUDING EQUALITY

Henceforth we shall only be concerned with the problem of validity for wffs in which the predicate variables appear only in a free form. These wffs are usually called the *wffs of the predicate calculus of first order*, or for short, the *wffs of first order*. With regard to our definition of validity we may also say that we shall be occupied only with the wffs which result from the wffs of first order by placing the universal quantifiers for the predicate variables before those quantifiers with scopes extending over the whole wff of first order.

The wffs with which we have to do, apart from those appearing in the proofs, are supposed to contain no free individual variables. For if they should occur, they may be bound by universal quantifiers.

## 1. Skolem's normal form

For proving general theorems about wffs of first order, it is convenient to make use of a special normal form, called the *Skolem normal form* (see Th. Skolem [2]). A Skolem normal form is a prenex normal form in which all existential quantifiers precede all universal ones.

*TI. For each wff of first order, one can construct another in a Skolem normal form such that both formulas are valid in the same domains, or both not valid in any domain.*

We start from a wff in prenex normal form. We may assume that the prefix of the wff begins with an existential quantifier; for if the wff, designated by $\mathfrak{A}$, begins with a universal quantifier, we replace $\mathfrak{A}$ by the equivalent wff $(Ex)(\mathfrak{A} \mathbin{\&} Gx \vee \overline{Gx})$, where $x$ and $G$ are supposed not to occur in $\mathfrak{A}$ (see $E22$ of III, § 1). The last wff can be brought into prenex normal form in a way such that $(\boldsymbol{Ex})$ is the first quantifier of the prefix.

Our wff thus begins with $n$ existential quantifiers ($n \geqslant 1$). By the degree of such a formula, we understand the number of universal quantifiers preceding at least one existential quantifier. If the degree is 0, nothing remains to be proved; otherwise, there is a universal quantifier immediately succeeding the $n$ existential quantifiers, and the wff has the form

$$\text{(j)} \qquad (Ex_1) \ldots (Ex_n)(y)\mathfrak{B}(x_1, \ldots, x_n, y).$$

$\mathfrak{B}$ contains only the free individual variables $x_1, \ldots, x_n, y$ and is in prenex normal form. Let $H$ be a $n+1$–adic predicate variable and $z$ an individual variable, both not occurring in $\mathfrak{B}$. We show that the wff

$$\text{(jj)} \quad (Ex_1) \ldots (Ex_n)(Ez)((\mathfrak{B}(x_1, \ldots, x_n, z) \;\&\; \overline{Hx_1 \ldots x_n z}) \vee (y)Hx_1 \ldots x_n y)$$

is valid in the same domains as (j).

Let $\Omega$ be an arbitrary assignment for the predicate variables of (jj) with the exception of $H$. We define an $n+1$–adic proportional function $\Psi$ in the relative domain $D$ in the following way. For any elements $a_1, \ldots, a_n, b$ of $D$ the value of $\Psi(a_1, \ldots, a_n, b)$ is the same as that of $\mathfrak{B}(a_1, \ldots, a_n, b)$ by $\Omega$. Let now (jj) be valid in $D$. There are then elements $a_1, \ldots, a_n, c$ such that

$$(\mathfrak{B}(a_1, \ldots, a_n, c) \;\&\; \overline{\Psi a_1 \ldots a_n c}) \vee (y)\Psi a_1 \ldots a_n y$$

is true by $\Omega$. Since $\mathfrak{B}(a_1, \ldots, a_n, c)$ and $\Psi a_1 \ldots a_n c$ get the same value by this assignment, $\mathfrak{B}(a_1, \ldots, a_n, c) \;\&\; \overline{\Psi a_1 \ldots a_n c}$ is false; consequently, $(y)\Psi a_1 \ldots a_n y$ is true. Owing to the definition of $\Psi$, this holds also for $(y)\mathfrak{B}(a_1, \ldots, a_n, y)$. Since $\Omega$ was arbitrary, this means that (j) is valid.

Let us now suppose (j) to be valid in a domain $D$. Let $\Omega$ be an arbitrary assignment for its predicate variables. There are then elements $a_1, \ldots, a_n$ of $D$ such that $(y)\mathfrak{B}(a_1, \ldots, a_n, y)$ is true by $\Omega$. Let $\Psi$ be an arbitrary $n+1$-adic propositional function over $D$. Either $(y)\Psi a_1 \ldots a_n y$ is true, in which case (jj) is true by the assignment $\Omega, \Psi$; or $(y)\Psi a_1 \ldots a_n y$ is false, and then there is an element $c$ of $D$ such that $\overline{\Psi a_1 \ldots a_n c}$ is true. Consequently, $\mathfrak{B}(a_1, \ldots, a_n, c)$ & $\overline{\Psi a_1 \ldots a_n c}$ is true by $\Omega$. Then (jj) is again true by $\Omega, \Psi$. (jj) is therefore valid in $D$ also.

We bring (jj) into prenex normal form. This can be done in a way such that the prefix begins with $(Ex_1) \ldots (Ex_n)(Ez)$, continues with the quantifiers of $\mathfrak{B}(x_1, \ldots, x_n, z)$ in unchanged succession and ends with the quantifier $(y)$. Obviously, the degree of this formula is lower by one than that of (j). By repeating this transformation we get a wff of degree 0.

## 2. Theorems about the validity of wffs not containing the sign of equality

In this § 2, we restrict ourselves to wffs not containing the sign of equality.

*TII. If a wff which has no prime formulas of the form* $\mathfrak{a} = \mathfrak{b}$ *is valid in a domain, it is also valid in any domain containing a smaller number of elements.*

Let $\mathfrak{A}(G_1, \ldots, G_n)$ be a wff valid in a domain $D_1$; let $D_2$ be a smaller domain. Further, let $\Psi_1, \ldots, \Psi_n$ be arbitrary propositional functions over $D_2$ suitable for assignments for $G_1, \ldots, G_n$. Since $D_1$ has more elements than $D_2$, we can define propositional functions $\Psi_1', \ldots, \Psi_n'$ over $D_1$ which are an extension of $\Psi_1, \ldots, \Psi_n$, as defined in the lemma of IV, § 1. Because $\mathfrak{A}(G_1, \ldots, G_n)$ is valid in $D_1$, $\mathfrak{A}(\Psi_1', \ldots, \Psi_n')$ is true in that domain. According to the mentioned lemma, $\mathfrak{A}(\Psi_1, \ldots, \Psi_n)$ is true in $D_2$; since $\Psi_1, \ldots, \Psi_n$ were arbitrary, $\mathfrak{A}(G_1, \ldots, G_n)$ is valid in $D_2$.

We now prove a remarkable theorem which was first obtained by L. Löwenheim [1] and the proof of which was afterwards considerably simplified by Th. Skolem [2] through application of his normal form. This theorem reads as follows:

*TIII. If a wff is valid in a denumerably infinite domain and is also valid in every finite domain, then it is universally valid.*

In this formulation of the theorem, the supposition that the wff does not contain the sign of equality is not necessary, as will be seen by the proof.

Let $\mathfrak{A}$ be a wff valid in a denumerably infinite domain and also in every finite domain and we may assume also that it is in Skolem normal form. $\mathfrak{A}$ has the form

$$(Ex_1) \dots (Ex\ )(y_1) \dots (y_n)\mathfrak{B}(x_1, \dots, x_m, y_1, \dots, y_n);$$

$\mathfrak{B}$ has no free individual variables besides $x_1, \dots, x_m, y_1, \dots, y_n$. Let $D$ be an arbitrary non-empty domain and $\Omega$ an arbitrary assignment for the free predicate variables of $\mathfrak{A}$ in $D$. We shall show that $\mathfrak{A}$ is true by $\Omega$ in $D$.

We prove this in an indirect way. Let us suppose that $\mathfrak{A}$ is false in $D$ by $\Omega$. We construct a sequence of finite subdomains of $D$, called $D_1, D_2, D_3, \dots$, with the following properties. Each $D_i$ is a subdomain of $D_{i+1}$. $D_1$ consists of just one arbitrarily chosen element of $D$. If $c_1, \dots, c_m$ are elements of $D_i$, there are always elements $d_1, \dots, d_n$ of $D$ such that $\mathfrak{B}(c_1, \dots, c_m, d_1, \dots, d_n)$ is false by $\Omega$; otherwise, $\mathfrak{A}$ would be true by $\Omega$. Then there is at least one $m$-tuple $c_1, \dots, c_m$ of elements of $D_i$ such that the elements $d_1, \dots, d_n$ belonging to them are not all elements of $D_i$. For if this were not the case, $\mathfrak{A}$ could not be valid in the finite domain $D_i$, contrary to our supposition. $D_{i+1}$ shall consist of all the elements of $D_i$ and of all the elements $d_1, \dots, d_n$ pertaining to some $m$-tuple $c_1, \dots, c_m$ of elements of $D_i$, in so far as these last elements are not already in $D_i$. $D_{i+1}$ has at least one element not contained in $D_i$. Let $D'$ be the domain containing any element of $D$ which is an element of some $D_i$. If $c_1, \dots, c_m$ is an arbitrary $m$-tuple of elements of $D'$, there are always elements $d_1, \dots, d_n$ of $D'$ such that $\mathfrak{B}(c_1, \dots, c_m, d_1, \dots, d_n)$ is false by $\Omega$; for the elements $c_1, \dots, c_m$ are all contained in some domain $D_i$, and the elements $d_1, \dots, d_n$ can be found in $D_{i+1}$. Then $\mathfrak{A}$ cannot be valid in $D'$, and since $D'$ is a denumerably infinite domain, this is a contradiction; therefore $\mathfrak{A}$ cannot be false in $D$ by $\Omega$.

Since $\Omega$ was arbitrary, $\mathfrak{A}$ is valid in $D$.

Combining TII and TIII we have:

*TIV. A wff which has no prime formulas of the form* $\mathfrak{a}=\mathfrak{b}$ *is universally valid, if it is valid in a denumerably infinite domain. If it is not valid in such a domain, validity at most exists in finite domains.*

## 3. Theorems about the validity of wffs which may contain the sign of equality

The theorems pronounced in § 2 do not all hold for any wffs in which the sign of equality occurs. TIII, it is true, remains in the general case, but not TII and TIV. Indeed, the wff $(Ex)(Ey)(\overline{x=y})$ for instance, is valid in all domains with two or more elements, but not valid in a domain with one single element. The following theorem states a relation between a wff containing the equality sign and a certain other one without this sign.

*TV. To every wff* $\mathfrak{A}$ *containing the sign of equality one can construct another one* $\mathfrak{B}$ *not containing the sign of equality which has the following relation to* $\mathfrak{A}$. *If* $\mathfrak{B}$ *is valid in a domain D,* $\mathfrak{A}$ *is valid in D. If* $\mathfrak{A}$ *is valid in a domain D and in all domains having a smaller cardinal number than D,* $\mathfrak{B}$ *is also valid in these domains.*

This theorem reduces the decision problem for wffs with prime formulas $\mathfrak{a}=\mathfrak{b}$ to that for wffs without such prime formulas, but only if we restrict ourselves to the form I or the form III of the problem. For the two wffs $\mathfrak{A}$ and $\mathfrak{B}$ mentioned in TV are both universally valid or both not universally valid; likewise, they are both valid in every finite domain, or both not valid. The theorem TV may be of some value in proving general theorems about the validity of wffs. When solving special cases of the decision problem, even if only the forms I or III of the problem are considered, it is not of much use; for the wff $\mathfrak{B}$ mentioned in the theorem has more quantifiers than $\mathfrak{A}$ and it has one dyadic predicate variable more. For instance, the decision problem for the wffs of the monadic predicate calculus with equality treated in § 3 of the preceding chapter is not reduced to the problem for wffs of the monadic predicate calculus without equality. but to the problem for wffs containing one dyadic predicate variable besides the monadic ones.

Let $\mathfrak{A}(G, =)$ be a wff with the free triadic predicate variable $G$ containing the equality sign, let $\mathfrak{A}(G, H)$ be the wff resulting from $\mathfrak{A}(G, =)$ by replacing all prime formulas $\mathfrak{a}=\mathfrak{b}$ by $H\mathfrak{a}\mathfrak{b}$.

Lastly, let $\mathfrak{B}(G, H)$ be an abbreviation for

$$(Ex)\overline{Hxx} \vee (Ex)(Ey)(Ez)(Hxy \;\&\; Hzy \;\&\; \overline{Hxz}) \vee (Ex)(Ey)(Ez)(Eu)$$
$$(Hxy \;\&\; (Gxzu \;\&\; \overline{Gyzu}) \vee (Gzxu \;\&\; \overline{Gzyu}) \vee (Gzux \;\&\; \overline{Gzuy})) \vee \mathfrak{A}(G, H).$$

We shall prove that $\mathfrak{A}(G, =)$ and $\mathfrak{B}(G, H)$ are in the relation described in TV.

Let $\mathfrak{B}(G, H)$ be valid in a domain $D$; then $\mathfrak{B}(G, =)$ is valid in $D$. Since

$$(Ex)(\overline{x=x}),\ (Ex)(Ey)(Ez)(x=y \ \&\ z=y \ \&\ \overline{x=z}),$$
$$(Ex)(Ey)(Ez)(Eu)(x=y \& (Gxzu \& \overline{Gyzu}) \vee (Gzxu \& \overline{Gzyu}) \vee (Gzux \& \overline{Gzuy}))$$

are false in $D$ by any assignment for $G$, $\mathfrak{A}(G, =)$ is valid in $D$.

Let $\mathfrak{A}(G, =)$ be valid in $D$ and in all domains having a smaller cardinal number and further, let $\Psi$ and $\Phi$ be arbitrary propositional functions over $D$ suitable for assignments to the predicate variables $G$ and $H$ of $\mathfrak{B}(G, H)$. We want to show that $\mathfrak{B}(\Psi, \Phi)$ is true in $D$. This is only doubtful if

$$(Ex)\overline{\Phi xx},\ (Ex)(Ey)(Ez)(\Phi xy \ \&\ \Phi zy \ \&\ \overline{\Phi xz})$$

and

$$(Ex)(Ey)(Ez)(Eu)(\Phi xy \ \&\ (\Psi xzu \ \&\ \overline{\Psi yzu}) \vee$$
$$\vee (\Psi zxu \ \&\ \overline{\Psi zyu}) \vee (\Psi zux \ \&\ \overline{\Psi zuy}))$$

are all false. In this case $\Phi$ is reflexive; i.e. for all elements $a$ of $D$ $\Phi aa$ is true. $\Phi$ is symmetric; i.e. if $\Phi ab$ is true, $\Phi ba$ is true. For $\Phi bb \ \&\ \Phi ab \ \&\ \overline{\Phi ba}$ is always false. $\Phi$ is transitive; i.e. if $\Phi ab$ and $\Phi bc$ are true, then $\Phi ac$ is true.

We divide the domain $D$ into several classes. Two elements $a$ and $b$ of $D$ belong to the same class if $\Phi ab$ is true; otherwise, they belong to different classes. If $\Psi abc$ is true, $\Psi a_1b_1c_1$ is true, provided that $a$ and $a_1$, $b$ and $b_1$, $c$ and $c_1$ belong to the same class; this follows because the disjunction term of $\mathfrak{B}(\Psi, \Phi)$ with the prefix

$$(Ex)(Ey)(Ez)(Eu)$$

is false. Let $D'$ be a subdomain of $D$ containing just one element of each class. To every element $a$ of $D$ we let correspond an element $a'$ of $D'$, namely the element $a'$ belonging to the same class as $a$. In $D'$, we define two propositional functions $\Phi'$ and $\Psi'$. For elements $a', b', c'$ of $D'$ $\Phi'a'b'(\Psi'a'b'c')$ is true, if and only if $\Phi a'b'(\Psi a'b'c')$ is true. Since $D'$ contains just one element of each class of $D$, $\Phi' a' b'$ is true, if and only if $a'$ and $b'$ are identical elements. On account of the stated properties of $\Phi$ and $\Psi$, the set of propositional functions $\Phi$, $\Psi$ in $D$ is an extension of the set $\Phi'$, $\Psi'$ in $D'$ in the sense of the lemma of IV, § 1. $\mathfrak{A}(\Psi', =)$ is true in $D'$ according to our supposition. Since $a' = b'$ and $\Phi' a' b'$ always have the same truth-value, $\mathfrak{A}(\Psi', \Phi')$ is true in $D'$. Applying the above-mentioned lemma, we recognize that $\mathfrak{A}(\Psi, \Phi)$ and therefore $\mathfrak{B}(\Psi, \Phi)$, is true in $D$.

Since $\Psi$ and $\Phi$ were arbitrary, $\mathfrak{B}(G, H)$ is valid in $D$ and is valid in all domains with a smaller cardinal number according to TII.

TV thus has been proven in case there is only one triadic predicate variable occurring in $\mathfrak{A}$. This restriction has been made only for the sake of a simpler presentation of the proof and is in no way essential. If there are more or other predicate variables in $\mathfrak{A}$, the only change in the construction of $\mathfrak{B}$ is that the disjunction term

$$(Ex)(Ey)(Ez)(Eu)(Hxy \mathbin{\&} (Gxzu \mathbin{\&} \overline{Gyzu}) \vee \vee (Gzxu \mathbin{\&} \overline{Gzyu}) \vee (Gzux \mathbin{\&} \overline{Gzuy}))$$

is replaced by several disjunction terms. For every monadic predicate variable $K$ there is a term $(Ex)(Ey)(Hxy \mathbin{\&} Kx \mathbin{\&} \overline{Ky})$ to be added, for every dyadic predicate variable $L$ a term $(Ex)(Ey)(Ez)(Hxy \mathbin{\&} (Lxz \mathbin{\&} \overline{Lyz}) \vee (Lzx \mathbin{\&} \overline{Lzy}))$, for every triadic predicate variable a term of the form mentioned above, and so forth. The proof is given in the same way.

For the wffs not containing the equality sign, the validity in any domain is known, provided this is so in finite and denumerably infinite domains. In the general case, the theorems so far derived do not permit such conclusions. It is sufficient, of course, to determine the validity in finite and denumerably infinite domains, if we are interested in knowing only whether a wff is universally valid or not. But if a wff is not universally valid, the knowledge of the validity in finite and denumerably infinite domains, for the present, does not give information about the validity in other domains.

To fill in this gap we prove the following two theorems.

*TVI. If a wff is valid in a denumerably infinite domain, it is valid in any infinite domain.*

Let $\mathfrak{A}$ be a wff which is valid in a denumerably infinite domain and which does not contain the predicate variables $G$ and $H$. $Inf(G, H)$ shall be an abbreviation for

$$(Ex)Gx \mathbin{\&} (x)(Ey)(\overline{Gx} \vee Hxy) \mathbin{\&} (x)(Ey)(Hyx \mathbin{\&} Gy) \mathbin{\&}$$
$$\mathbin{\&} (x)(y)(z)((\overline{Hxy} \vee \overline{Hxz} \mathbin{\&} \overline{Hyx} \vee \overline{Hzx}) \vee y=z).$$

$Inf(G, H)$ is satisfiable in all infinite domains, but not in any finite domain. For $Inf(\Psi, \Phi)$ is true in a domain $D$, if and only if there is a non-empty subdomain of $D$ consisting of the elements for which $\Psi(a)$ is true such that the elements of this subdomain can be put into one-to-one correspondence with the elements of $D$ by means of $\Phi$. This is the definition of an infinite domain set up by R. Dedekind. $\overline{Inf(G, H)}$ is valid in any finite domain, but not in an infinite domain. The wff $\overline{Inf(G, H)} \vee \mathfrak{A}$ is valid in any finite domain and in a denumerably infinite domain and according to TIII, it is universally valid. Because $\overline{Inf(G, H)}$ is not valid in an infinite domain, $\mathfrak{A}$ is valid in any infinite domain.

*TVII. If a wff is valid in an infinite domain, it is valid in a denumerably infinite domain and there is a finite number k such that the wff is valid in all finite domains with k or more elements.*

The theorem, however, provides no way of determining this number $k$ for a given wff.

For the proof of the theorem we shall suppose that the elements of the infinite domain in question are the ordinals preceding a certain transfinite ordinal $b$; such a domain will be designated by $D_b$. This is equivalent to the assumption that the infinite domain can be well-ordered, for the elements of any well-ordered domain can be put into one-to-one correspondence with those of a certain domain $D_b$.

Ordered $k$-tuples $(a_1, \ldots, a_k)$ of ordinals can be well-ordered by a relation $\underset{k}{<}$. The definition is: $(a_1, \ldots, a_k) \underset{k}{<} (b_1, \ldots, b_k)$ if Max $(a_1, \ldots$ $\ldots, a_k) <$ Max $(b_1, \ldots, b_k)$; or Max $(a_1, \ldots, a_k) =$ Max $(b_1, \ldots, b_k)$ and $a_1 < b_1$; or Max $(a_1, \ldots, a_k) =$ Max $(b_1, \ldots, b_k)$, $a_1 = b_1$ and $a_2 < b_2, \ldots$; or Max $(a_1, \ldots, a_k) =$ Max $(b_1, \ldots, b_k)$, $a_1 = b_1, \ldots, a_{k-1} = b_{k-1}$ and $a_k < b_k$.

Max $(a_1, \ldots, a_k)$ is the element among $a_1, \ldots, a_k$ which does not precede any other.

We further define a function $\varphi$ for ordinals which assigns the ordinal $\varphi(a_1, \ldots, a_m)$ to an $m$-tuple $(a_1, \ldots, a_m)$ of ordinals and which depends on the number $n$. $\varphi$ is defined by transfinite induction. If 1 is the first ordinal, $\varphi(1, \ldots, 1)$ is the $n^{th}$ successor of 1. Let $\varphi$ be defined for all $(a_1, \ldots, a_m)$ with $(a_1, \ldots, a_m) \underset{m}{<} (d_1, \ldots, d_m)$ and let $e$ be the first ordinal succeeding all these ordinals $\varphi(a_1, \ldots, a_m)$; $\varphi(d_1, \ldots, d_m)$ is then the $n^{th}$ successor of $e$. Obviously, $\varphi(a_1, \ldots, a_m) > a_i$ and $\varphi(a_1, \ldots, a_m) > \varphi(b_1, \ldots, b_m)$ if $(a_1, \ldots, a_m) \underset{m}{>} (b_1, \ldots, b_m)$.

If every subdomain of an infinite domain $D_b$ consisting of the elements preceding a certain element has a cardinal number less than $D_b$, then $\varphi(a_1, \ldots, a_m)$ is an element of $D_b$ if $a_1, \ldots, a_m$ are elements of $D_b$. This is shown by transfinite induction. Indeed, this is obvious for $\varphi(1, \ldots, 1)$, since $D_b$ cannot have a last element. It may be true for all $m$-tuples $(a_1, \ldots, a_m)$ preceding a certain $m$-tuple $(d_1, \ldots, d_m)$. All these $\varphi(a_1, \ldots, a_m)$ precede a certain element of $D_b$; for the set of these $\varphi(a_1, \ldots, a_m)$ has a lower cardinal number than $D_b$ and, according to a well-known theorem of set theory, the elements of any subset of $D_b$ which has a cardinal number less than $D_b$ must all precede a certain element of $D_b$. Therefore, $\varphi(d_1, \ldots, d_m)$ is in $D_b$ also.

Let $\mathfrak{A}$ or $(Ex_1)\ldots(Ex_m)(y_1)\ldots(y_n)\mathfrak{B}(x_1, \ldots, x_m, y_1, \ldots, y_n)$ be a wff in Skolem normal form. For the sake of a simple presentation of the proof we shall restrict ourselves to the case in which $\mathfrak{A}$ contains only the dyadic predicate variables $G_1, \ldots, G_l$. But this is of no consequence; $\overline{\mathfrak{A}}$ is equivalent to

$$(x_1)\ldots(x_m)(Ey_1)\ldots(Ey_n)\overline{\mathfrak{B}(x_1, \ldots, x_m, y_1, \ldots, y_n)}.$$

Let $\mathfrak{K}$ be a subdomain of a domain $D_b$. $\overline{\mathfrak{A}}$ is called *partially satisfiable in $D_b$ with respect to* $\mathfrak{K}$ if there are propositional functions $\Psi_1, \ldots, \Psi_l$ in $D_b$ such that for arbitrary $a_1, \ldots, a_m$ (but all taken from $\mathfrak{K}$), there are elements $b_1, \ldots, b_n$ of $D_b$, all preceding or equal to $\varphi(a_1, \ldots, a_m)$, for which $\mathfrak{B}(a_1, \ldots, a_m, b_1, \ldots, b_n)$ is false by $\Psi_1, \ldots, \Psi_l$. We now prove two lemmas.

Lemma 1. Let $\overline{\mathfrak{A}}$ be satisfiable in a denumerably infinite domain, or for every finite number $p$, let there be a finite domain with $p$ or more elements such that $\overline{\mathfrak{A}}$ is satisfiable in that domain. If $\mathfrak{K}$ is a finite subdomain of a domain $D_b$, then $\overline{\mathfrak{A}}$ is partially satisfiable in $D_b$ with respect to $\mathfrak{K}$.

The elements of $\mathfrak{K}$ may be $d_1, \ldots, d_k$, enumerated in their right order. There is a finite or denumerably infinite subdomain of $D_b$ containing the elements $d_1, \ldots, d_k$ such that $\overline{\mathfrak{A}}$ is satisfiable in that subdomain. There are then dyadic propositional functions $\Psi_1, \ldots, \Psi_l$ in $D_b$ and elements $b_1, \ldots, b_n$ for every $a_1, \ldots, a_m$ taken from the set $(d_1, \ldots, d_k)$, such that $\mathfrak{B}(a_1, \ldots, a_m, b_1, \ldots, b_n)$ is false by $\Psi_1, \ldots, \Psi_l$. For each $m$-tuple $(a_1, \ldots, a_m)$ we select a special set $b_1, \ldots, b_n$. By a one-to-one correspondence of the elements of $D_b$ with themselves (the element $d_1$ corresponding to itself), we can find an assignment $\Psi_1', \ldots, \Psi_l'$ of the aforesaid kind such that the elements $b_1, \ldots, b_n$ belonging to $(d_1, \ldots, d_1)$ are $\leqslant \varphi(d_1, \ldots, d_1)$. By a further one-to-one correspondence of the elements of $D_b$ by which all elements preceding or equal to $\varphi(d_1, \ldots, d_l)$ and the element $d_2$ correspond to themselves, we get an assignment $\Psi_1'', \ldots, \Psi_l''$ so that for every $b_i$ belonging to $(d_1, \ldots, d_1, d_2)$, $b_i \leqslant \varphi(d_1, \ldots, d_1, d_2)$. This procedure is continued and after a finite number of steps we find an assignment for $G_1, \ldots, G_l$ such that $\overline{\mathfrak{A}}$ is partially satisfiable in $D_b$ with respect to $(d_1, \ldots, d_k)$.

Lemma 2. Let $\overline{\mathfrak{A}}$ be partially satisfiable in $D_b$ with respect to any finite subdomain $\mathfrak{K}$ of $D_b$; then $\overline{\mathfrak{A}}$ is satisfiable in $D_b$.

We shall assume that $\varphi(a_1, \ldots, a_m)$ is always in $D_b$ if $a_1, \ldots, a_m$ are elements of $D_b$. This is no restriction on the use of the lemma; for there is else a domain $D_{b'}$ with $b' < b$ which has the cardinal number of $D_b$ and is such that all proper subdomains $D_c$ of $D_{b'}$ have a cardinal number less than $D_{b'}$.

If 2 is the second element of $D_b$, $\overline{\mathfrak{A}}$ is partially satisfiable in $D_b$ with respect to any subdomain of $D_b$ consisting of the element $< 2$ and a finite number of other elements. Let $d$ be an element of $D_b$ and let $\overline{\mathfrak{A}}$ be partially satisfiable in $D_b$ with respect to any subdomain of $D_b$ consisting of the elements $< d'$ with $d' < d$ and a finite number of other elements. $\overline{\mathfrak{A}}$ is then partially satisfiable with respect to any subdomain of $D_b$ containing the elements $< d$ and a finite number of other elements.

To prove this, we distinguish two cases. 1) $d$ may have an immediate predecessor $d'$. According to our supposition, $\overline{\mathfrak{A}}$ is partially satisfiable with respect to the elements $< d'$ and a finite number of other elements; therefore, it is partially satisfiable with respect to the elements $< d$ and a finite number of other elements. 2) Suppose $d$ to have no immediate predecessor; let $e_1, \ldots, e_k$ be arbitrary elements not preceding $d$. For every $d' < d$ we select a set of propositional functions $\Psi_{1d'}, \ldots, \Psi_{ld'}$ by which $\overline{\mathfrak{A}}$ is partially satisfiable with respect to the elements $< d'$ and $e_1, \ldots, e_k$. We now define other dyadic propositional functions $\Phi_1, \ldots, \Phi_l$ over $D_b$ by transfinite induction. $\Phi_1(1, 1)$ is true if for every $d' < d$ there is a $d''$ with $d' < d'' < d$ such that $\Psi_{1d''}(1, 1)$ is true; otherwise, $\Phi_1(1, 1)$ is false. $\Phi_1, \ldots, \Phi_l$ may be defined for all ordered pairs $(a_1, a_2)$ for which $(a_1, a_2) \underset{2}{<} (c_1, c_2)$, and $\Phi_i(i < j;\ 1 \leqslant j \leqslant l)$ for $(c_1, c_2)$. $\Phi_j(c_1, c_2)$. is true if for every $d' < d$ there is a $d''$ with $d' < d'' < d$ such that the values of $\Psi_{1d''} \ldots, \Psi_{ld''}$ coincide with the values of $\Phi_1, \ldots, \Phi_l$ so far as these last are fixed, and such that $\Psi_{jd''}(c_1, c_2)$ is true; otherwise $\Phi_j(c_1, c_2)$ is false. Let $(a_1, \ldots, a_m)$ be an $m$-tuple of elements of $D_b$ such that all $a_i$ precede $d$ or are equal to one of the elements $e_1, \ldots, e_k$. For every $d' < d$ there is a $d''$ with $d' < d'' < d$ such that $\Psi_{1d''}, \ldots, \Psi_{ld''}$ have the same values as $\Phi_1, \ldots, \Phi_l$ for all ordered pairs $(c_1, c_2)$ for which Max $(c_1, c_2) \leqslant \varphi(a_1, \ldots, a_m)$, and such that there are elements $b_1, \ldots, b_n$ (none of them succeeding $\varphi(a_1, \ldots, a_m)$) for which $\mathfrak{B}(a_1, \ldots, a_m, b_1, \ldots, b_n)$ is false by $\Psi_{1d''}, \ldots, \Psi_{ld''}$. The last formula is then also false by $\Phi_1, \ldots, \Phi_l$. Thus also in case 2) $\overline{\mathfrak{A}}$ is partially satisfiable with respect to the elements $< d$ and a finite number of other elements.

It follows by transfinite induction that $\overline{\mathfrak{A}}$ is partially satisfiable in $D_b$ with respect to any subdomain of $D_b$ consisting of the elements preceding a certain element. In the same way as above in case 2), the set $e_1, \ldots, e_k$ now being vacuous, we conclude that $\overline{\mathfrak{A}}$ is partially satisfiable in $D_b$ with respect to $D_b$ itself. This means that $\overline{\mathfrak{A}}$ is satisfiable in $D_b$.

Combining lemma 1 and 2 we get: If $\overline{\mathfrak{A}}$ is satisfiable in a denumerably infinite domain, or if for every finite number $p$ there is a finite domain with $p$ or more elements such that $\overline{\mathfrak{A}}$ is satisfiable in that domain, $\overline{\mathfrak{A}}$ is satisfiable in every well-ordered infinite domain. If we express this statement in terms of validity instead of satisfiability, we have our theorem TVII.

Theorems VI and VII now yield the result that to determine the domains in which all wffs are valid, we need only investigate the validity for finite and denumerably infinite domains.

*If a wff is valid in a denumerably infinite domain, validity exists in all domains with the possible exception of a finite number of finite domains. If a wff is not valid in a denumerably infinite domain, it is not valid in any infinite domain, but may be valid (if validity exists at all in some domain) in all or in some finite domains.*

For the solution of special cases of the decision problem these theorems are of importance, since they permit the *restriction to the domain of the natural numbers and to finite domains of natural numbers* when determining the validity of a wff. This results in a considerable facilitation.

# VI

# SOLUTION OF THE DECISION PROBLEM FOR WFFS WITH SPECIAL PREFIXES

## 1. Remarks on the selection of special cases of the decision problem

In the following, we give a report on special classes of wffs without bound predicate variables for which a solution of the decision problem has been obtained apart from the solution for wffs containing only monadic predicate variables. Such a report cannot be complete in the sense that it comprises all wffs, the validity of which may actually be determined. Every proven mathematical theorem yields the validity of some wff. The relation between mathematical problems and special cases of the decision problem is given by D. Hilbert and W. Ackermann [1],(chapter III, § 11). There are certain elementary parts of mathematics, such as elementary algebra, for which even a complete solution of the decision problem has been reached (see C. H. Langford [1, 2], M. Presburger [1], A. Tarski [2], J. C. C. McKinsey [1], W. Smielew [1], Th. Skolem [4]). But in general, the wffs the validity of which is known by mathematics are of a very different character. Some of them have a rather complicated logical structure while the validity of others which are relatively simply constructed is unknown.

For a systematic treatment of the decision problem from a logical point of view, it is best to consider classes of wffs which have a common logical structure. It is convenient to assume the wffs to be in prenex normal form. Special classes of wffs may be obtained by confining ourselves: 1) *to certain classes of prefixes*, 2) *to special structures of the matrix*, 3) *to occurring predicate variables limited as to their number and character.*

Not every restriction of this kind will lead to classes of wffs for which a complete solution of the decision problem may be taken into consideration. For instance, it is useless to try to solve the decision problem for all wffs with a prefix $(Ex_1)\ldots(Ex_m)(y_1)\ldots(y_n)$, since all wffs can be brought into Skolem normal form and therefore, the solution of the problem for these wffs would include a general solution of the decision problem for wffs without bound predicate variables. A general solution of the decision problem for wffs of this type is excluded by the papers mentioned in chapter II, § 5. There are other classes of prefixes such that every wff can be transformed into another one having a prefix of the class. The reduction of all wffs to formulas with a special kind of prefix may be of importance for proving general theorems about wffs, as has been seen by the utility of the Skolem normal form in deriving the general theorems of the previous chapter. We shall only mention some of these *reduction theorems,* for they generally lend no assistance in the solution of special cases of the decision problem; but they give warning against undertaking too much.

Every wff can be reduced to a corresponding one having the prefix

$(Ex)(Ey)(Ez)(u_1)\ldots(u_m)$ (see K. Gödel [3]), or
$(Ex)(Ey)(z_1)\ldots(z_m)(Eu)$ (see L. Kalmar [9]), or
$(Ex)(Ey)(z)(Eu_1)\ldots(Eu_m)$ (see J. Pepis [2, 3]), or
$(x)(Ey)(z)(Eu_1)\ldots(Eu_m)$ (see W. Ackermann [4]), or
$(Ex)(Ey)(Ez)(u)$ or $(Ex)(Ey)(z)(Eu)$ (see J. Suranyi [1]), or
$(Ex)(y)(z)(Eu)(Ev)$ or $(x)(Ey)(z)(Eu)(Ev)$ (see J. Suranyi [2]).

As regards the first four classes of prefixes, no general solution of the decision problem is even possible if the predicate variables occurring are restricted to a dyadic one; for L. Kalmar and J. Suranyi have shown that every wff can also be given such a form (see L. Kalmar [8, 9]); L. Kalmar and J. Suranyi [1, 2]).

The chief results in the solution of special cases of the decision problem are solutions for special classes of prefixes. These solutions have been given in literature for wffs not containing equality in general, we extend them to wffs with equality. For some of these classes, the solution thereby gets more complicated. Setting aside the cases for which a solution can be reached in a more or less trivial way, the author has been trying to give a systematic treatment by reducing the special decision problems to those of the monadic predicate calculus.

## 2. Solution for wffs having prefixes consisting solely of universal quantifiers

Let the wff be of the form $(x_1) \dots (x_m)\mathfrak{A}(x_1, \dots, x_m)$, where $\mathfrak{A}$ contains no quantifiers.

*For a wff of this kind, validity need only be determined for domains with* $1, \dots, m$ *elements. For validity exists in a domain with more than m elements, if and only if it exists in a domain with m elements. If the wff is valid in a domain with m elements, it is universally valid.*

Let $D_1$ be a domain with $k$ elements ($k \leqslant m$) and a subdomain of $D_2$. Further, let the wff be valid in $D_2$ and let $a_1, \dots, a_m$ be an arbitrary ordered $m$-tuple of elements of $D_1$. $\mathfrak{A}(a_1, \dots, a_m)$ is true by any assignment of propositional functions over $D_1$ because it is true in $D_2$ by an assignment of propositional functions which have the same values as the functions over $D_1$, provided only elements of $D_1$ are concerned.

On the other hand, the wff may be valid in $D_1$, the last domain having in this case exactly $m$ elements. Let $b_1, \dots, b_m$ be an arbitrary tuple of elements of $D_2$. For the valuation of the formula $\mathfrak{A}(b_1, \dots, b_m)$ in $D_2$, only the values of the propositional functions for $b_i$ and tuples of $b_i$ are of consequence. Since the elements $b_1, \dots, b_m$ are elements (not necessarily the only elements) of a domain with $m$ elements and since validity exists in this domain, $\mathfrak{A}(b_1, \dots, b_m)$ is true in $D_2$ however the assignments for the predicate variables are chosen.

*The decision problem for wffs with only universal quantifiers can also be solved in another way, namely by constructing an equivalent equality formula.* Properly spoken, the wff resulting from the given one by placing universal quantifiers for all predicate variables at the beginning of the wff, is equivalent to the equality formula; for the predicate and the individual quantifiers can change their places, and then the predicate variables can be eliminated by applying $E25$ of IV, § 2.

## 3. Solution for wffs having prefixes consisting solely of existential quantifiers

Let the wff be of the form $(Ex_1) \ldots (Ex_m)\mathfrak{A}(x_1, \ldots, x_m)$ where $\mathfrak{A}(x_1, \ldots, x_m)$ contains no quantifiers and no individual variables besides $x_1, \ldots, x_m$.

*A wff of this kind is universally valid, if it is valid in the domain with one element. If it is valid in some domain, it is valid in any domain with a larger number of elements.*

Let $D_1$ be a subdomain of $D_2$ and let the wff be valid in $D_1$. If we have an arbitrary assignment $\Omega$ for the predicate variables in $D_2$, there is a corresponding assignment $\Omega'$ in $D_1$, namely that one formed by the propositional functions over $D_1$ coinciding with those over $D_2$, so far as elements of $D_1$ are involved. There exist elements $a_1, \ldots, a_m$ of $D_1$ such that $\mathfrak{A}(a_1, \ldots, a_m)$ is true by $\Omega'$. Obviously, $\mathfrak{A}(a_1, \ldots, a_m)$ is true by $\Omega$.

*For the wffs with only existential quantifiers not containing equality, the decision problem in the form II is solved by use of TII of V, § 2. Such a wff is either universally valid or valid in no domain at all. Valuation in a domain of one element reveals which of the two cases presents itself.*

For the wffs containing equality, the domains in which they are valid are not so easily determined. According to V, § 3, such a wff is either universally valid or valid in no domain at all; or there is a finite number $k$ such that the wff is not valid in domains with less than $k$ elements and is valid in any domain with $k$ or more elements. But hitherto, we have not been able to decide under which of the last two cases the wff falls if the first one is excluded. Nor can we at this point effectively determine the number $k$ if the wff should fall under the third case.

In the following solution of the problem, we shall restrict ourselves to wffs with only monadic and dyadic predicate variables. This restriction is in no way essential. The dyadic predicate variables occurring in $\mathfrak{A}(x_1, \ldots, x_m)$ may be $G_1, \ldots, G_l$. We first prove a lemma.

Lemma. Let $\varphi_1, \ldots, \varphi_l, \chi_1, \ldots, \chi_l$ be functions, the domains and ranges of which are the non-negative integers. They are defined by the following simultaneous recursions:

$$\chi_r(0, q) = q, \ \varphi_r(0, q) = q \quad (r = 1, \ldots, l);$$
$$\chi_1(p+1, q) = \varphi_l(p, 1+2q);$$
$$\chi_{r+1}(p+1, q) = \varphi_r(p+1, 2q) \quad (r = 1, \ldots, l-1);$$
$$\varphi_r(p+1, q) = \chi_r(p+1, 2q) \quad (r = 1, \ldots, l).$$

We then assert I and II.

I. Let $\Gamma_1, \ldots, \Gamma_l$ be dyadic propositional functions over a domain $D$ with $\chi_r(p, q)$ elements which may be natural numbers. Then there exists a subdomain $D_1$ of $D$ with $p+q$ elements $a_1, \ldots, a_p, b_1, \ldots, b_q$ (written in their natural order) and the following property. $\Gamma_j(a_i, c)$ has the same value for all $c$ of $D_1$ with $a_i < c$, provided that $i < p$, or $i = p$ and $j \leqslant r$. $\Gamma_j(c, a_i)$ has the same value for all $c$ of $D_1$ with $a_i < c$, provided that $i < p$, or $i = p$ and $j < r$.

II. If we replace $\chi_r(p, q)$ by $\varphi_r(p, q)$ in the foregoing statement, the same is asserted, but then the last $j < r$ can be replaced by $j \leqslant r$.

We prove the lemma by induction corresponding to the recursions of $\varphi_r$ and $\chi_r$. If $p = 0$, there is nothing to be proven. We suppose II to be proven for $p$ and an arbitrary $r$ and $q$. Let $D$ be a domain with $\varphi_l(p, 1+2q)$ or $\chi_1(p+1, q)$ elements in which propositional functions $\Gamma_1, \ldots, \Gamma_l$ are defined. $D$ has a subdomain $(a_1, \ldots, a_p, b_1, \ldots, b_{1+2q})$ according to II. Among the elements $b_2, \ldots, b_{1+2q}$, there are at least $q$ elements $c_1, \ldots, c_q$ such that $\Gamma_1(b_1, c_i)$ has the same value for all $c_i$; $(a_1, \ldots, a_p, b_1, c_1, \ldots, c_q)$ is then a subdomain of $D$ corresponding to $\chi_1(p+1, q)$, according to I. II may be proved for $\varphi_r(p+1, q)$, where $q$ is arbitrary. A domain with $\varphi_r(p+1, 2q)$ or $\chi_{r+1}(p+1, q)$ elements, in which propositional functions $\Gamma_i$ are defined, then has a subdomain $(a_1, \ldots, a_{p+1}, b_1, \ldots, b_{2q})$ such that the values of $\Gamma_j(a_i, c)$ and of $\Gamma_j(c, a_i)$ depend only on $a_i$ if $a_i < c$ and $i \leqslant p$, or $a_i < c$, $i = p+1$, and $j \leqslant r$. Among these $b_1, \ldots, b_{2q}$, there are at least $q$ elements $c_1, \ldots, c_q$ such that the value of $\Gamma_{r+1}(a_{p+1}, c_i)$ depends only upon $a_{p+1}$. $(a_1, \ldots, a_{p+1}, c_1, \ldots, c_q)$ is a domain corresponding to $\chi_{r+1}(p+1, q)$, according to I. Let I be proved for $\chi_r(p+1, q)$, where $q$ is arbitrary. If $\Gamma_1, \ldots, \Gamma_l$ are defined in a domain with $\chi_r(p+1, 2q)$ or $\varphi_r(p+1, q)$ elements, this domain has a subdomain $(a_1, \ldots, a_{p+1}, b_1, \ldots, b_{2q})$, according to I. By the same method, we find a domain

$(a_1, \ldots, a_{p+1}, c_1, \ldots, c_i)$ corresponding to $\varphi_r(p+1, q)$, according to II.

We return to our wff $(Ex_1) \ldots (Ex_m)\mathfrak{A}(x_1, \ldots, x_m)$. Let $\mathfrak{B}(x_1, \ldots, x_m)$ be the disjunction of all wffs $\mathfrak{A}(\mathfrak{a}_1, \ldots, \mathfrak{a}_m)$ where $\mathfrak{a}_1, \ldots, \mathfrak{a}_m$ are arbitrary variables from the set $(x_1, \ldots, x_m)$ taken in any order, with or without repetitions. If $(Ex_1) \ldots (Ex_m)\mathfrak{A}(x_1, \ldots, x_m)$ is valid in some domain, $(Ex_1) \ldots (Ex_m)\mathfrak{B}(x_1, \ldots, x_m)$ is valid, and conversely.

We now construct a third formula with the prefix $(Ex_1) \ldots (Ex_m)$ which has only monadic predicate variables. In $\mathfrak{B}(x_1, \ldots, x_m)$, we replace every prime formula $G_i x_p x_p$ by $H_i x_p$, every prime formula $G_i x_p x_q$ $(p<q)$ by $K_i x_p$ and every prime formula $G_i x_p x_q$ $(p>q)$ by $L_i x_q$. $\mathfrak{B}(x_1, \ldots, x_m)$ is then transformed into a wff $\mathfrak{C}(x_1, \ldots, x_m)$ which contains only the monadic predicate variables $H_i, K_i, L_i$ $(i=1, \ldots, l)$ and the monadic predicate variables already occurring in $\mathfrak{B}(x_1, \ldots, x_m)$ The last variables are supposed to be different from $H_i, K_i, L_i$.

The following relations hold between $(Ex_1), \ldots (Ex_m)\mathfrak{B}(x_1, \ldots, x_m)$ and $(Ex_1) \ldots (Ex_m)\mathfrak{C}(x_1, \ldots, x_m)$.

a) If $(Ex_1) \ldots (Ex_m)\mathfrak{B}(x_1, \ldots, x_m)$ is valid in a finite domain with $m$ or more elements, then $(Ex_1) \ldots (Ex_m)\mathfrak{C}(x_1, \ldots, x_m)$ is valid in this domain also.

The elements of this domain be natural numbers. Let $\Phi_1, \ldots, \Phi_l, \Psi_1, \ldots, \Psi_l, \Theta_1, \ldots, \Theta_l$ be an arbitrary assignment for the predicate variables $H_i, K_i, L_i$, and $\Omega$ a similar assignment for the other monadic predicate variables. We define dyadic propositional functions $\Gamma_1, \ldots, \Gamma_l$ over the domain. For any $a$ and $b$, $\Gamma_i(a, b)$ has the same value as $\Phi_i(a)$ or $\Psi_i(a)$ or $\Theta_i(b)$, according as $a=b$ or $a<b$ or $a>b$. Since $(Ex_1) \ldots (Ex_m)\mathfrak{B}(x_1, \ldots, x_m)$ is valid in the domain, there are elements $a_1, \ldots, a_m$ such that $\mathfrak{B}(a_1, \ldots, a_m)$ is true by $\Gamma_1, \ldots \Gamma_l\, \Omega$. We now take a set $c_1, \ldots, c_m$ of elements of the domain such that $c_i < c_{i+1}$ and which is such that the elements $a_1, \ldots, a_m$ are contained among $c_1, \ldots, c_m$. Such a set can be found, for the domain has at least $m$ elements. $\mathfrak{B}(c_1, \ldots, c_m)$ contains the disjunction term $\mathfrak{B}(a_1, \ldots, a_m)$ and is therefore also true by $\Gamma_1, \ldots, \Gamma_l, \Omega$. $\mathfrak{C}(c_1, \ldots, c_m)$ is then true by $\Phi_1, \ldots, \Phi_l$, $\Psi_1, \ldots, \Psi_l$, $\Theta_1, \ldots, \Theta_l$, $\Omega$, since the prime formulas of $\mathfrak{C}(c_1, \ldots, c_m)$ receive the same value by this assignment as the corresponding ones of $\mathfrak{B}(c_1, \ldots, c_m)$ by $\Gamma_1, \ldots, \Gamma_l$, $\Omega$. Since the assignment for

$(Ex_1) \dots (Ex_m)\mathfrak{C}(x_1, \dots, x_m)$ was arbitrary, this wff is valid in the domain.

b) If $(Ex_1) \dots (Ex_m)\mathfrak{C}(x_1, \dots, x_m)$ is valid in a finite domain with $k$ elements $(k \geqslant m)$, $(Ex_1) \dots (Ex_m)\mathfrak{B}(x_1, \dots, x_m)$ is valid in a domain with $\varphi_l(k, 0)$ elements.

Let $D$ be a domain with $\varphi_l(k, 0)$ elements. $\Gamma_1, \dots, \Gamma_l, \Omega$ are assignments in this domain for $G_1, \dots, G_l$ and the monadic predicate variables of $\mathfrak{B}(x_1, \dots, x_m)$. There is then a subdomain $D_1$ of $D$ with $k$ elements such that the value of $\Gamma_j(a, b)$ $(j = 1, \dots, b)$ in this domain depends only upon $a$ if $a < b$, and only upon $b$ if $b < a$. We define monadic propositional functions $\Phi_i, \Psi_i, \Theta_i$ $(i = 1, \dots, l)$ over $D_1$ such that $\Phi_i(a)$, $\Psi_i(a)$ and $\Theta_i(a)$ always have the same value respectively, as $\Gamma_i(a, a)$, $\Gamma_i(a, b)$ for $a < b$ and $\Gamma_i(b, a)$ for $a < b$. Values of $\Psi_i$ and $\Theta_i$ not determined thereby may be supplied in an arbitrary way. According to our supposition, there are elements $a_1, \dots, a_m$ of $D_1$ such that $\mathfrak{C}(a_1, \dots, a_m)$ is true by $\Phi_i, \Psi_i, \Theta_i, \Omega$. Let $c_1, \dots, c_m$ be a set of elements of $D_1$ such that $c_i < c_{i+1}$ and such that $a_1, \dots, a_m$ are contained among $c_1, \dots, c_m$. Since $\mathfrak{C}(c_1, \dots, c_m)$ contains the disjunction term $\mathfrak{C}(a_1, \dots, a_m)$, $\mathfrak{C}(c_1, \dots, c_m)$ is true by $\Phi_i, \Psi_i, \Theta_i, \Omega$. $\mathfrak{B}(c_1, \dots, c_m)$ is then true in $D$ by $\Gamma_1, \dots, \Gamma_l, \Omega$, for the valuation of all prime formulas is the same as that of the corresponding prime formulas of $\mathfrak{C}(c_1, \dots, c_m)$ by the previous assignment. Since $\Gamma_1, \dots, \Gamma_l, \Omega$ were arbitrary,

$$(Ex_1) \dots (Ex_m)\mathfrak{B}(x_1, \dots, x_m)$$

is valid in $D$.

In a) and b) we may substitute $(Ex_1) \dots (Ex_m)\mathfrak{A}(x_1, \dots, x_m)$ for $(Ex_1) \dots (Ex_m)\mathfrak{B}(x_1, \dots, x_m)$, since both wffs are valid in the same domains.

The problem of determining the domains in which

$$(Ex_1) \dots (Ex_m)\mathfrak{A}(x_1, \dots, x_m)$$

is valid, is now generally solved. $(Ex_1) \dots (Ex_m)\mathfrak{C}(x_1, \dots, x_m)$ is a wff with only monadic predicate variables for which this problem can be solved with the methods of IV, § 3.

*Either* $(Ex_1) \dots (Ex_m)\mathfrak{C}(x_1, \dots, x_m)$ *is valid in no domain at all,* *in which case according to a), $(Ex_1) \dots (Ex_m)\mathfrak{A}(x_1, \dots, x_m)$ is valid in no domain; or there is a finite domain in which $(Ex_1)\dots(Ex_m)\mathfrak{C}(x_1,\dots,x_m)$ is valid. Let the smallest domain of this kind, which can be determined, have $p$ elements, and let $k$ be $Max\,(p, m)$. Since $(Ex_1)\dots(Ex_m)\mathfrak{C}(x_1,\dots,x_m)$ is valid in a domain with $k$ elements, $(Ex_1) \dots (Ex_m)\mathfrak{A}(x_1, \dots, x_m)$ is valid in all domains with $\varphi_l(k, 0)$ and more elements according to b). To completely determine the domains in which $(Ex_1)\dots(Ex_m)\mathfrak{A}(x_1,\dots,x_m)$ is valid, validity has still to be investigated for domains with 1, 2, ..., $\varphi_l(k, 0)-1$ elements. This may be done with the methods of I, § 2.*

## 4. Reduction of the decision problem for wffs with certain prefixes to that for wffs with simpler prefixes

Before proceeding to the solution of the decision problem for other classes of prefixes it is useful to derive a certain reduction theorem due in the general form stated here to L. Kalmar [4] and used before in a more special form by W. Ackermann [1].

*Let $\mathfrak{A}$ be a wff in prenex normal form without free individual variables and with the prefix $(x_1)\dots(x_m)(Ey_1) \dots (Ey_n)(z_1) \dots (z_k)$. The decision problem for $\mathfrak{A}$ can be solved if it can be solved for wffs with a prefix $(Ey_1) \dots (Ey_n)(z_1) \dots (z_r)$. Here, $n$ is the same number as before, while $r$ is arbitrary. If $k=0$, $r$ is 0.*

To exhibit the idea of the proof, it will be sufficient to carry it through for the case that $\mathfrak{A}$ contains only monadic and dyadic predicate variables, namely the monadic predicate variables $G_1, \dots, G_p$ and the dyadic ones $H_1, \dots, H_q$.

$\mathfrak{A}$ is transformed into a wff $\mathfrak{B}$ in the following way. Every prime formula $G_i\mathfrak{a}$ is replaced by $\overline{\mathfrak{a}=x_1} \vee X_i \;\&\; \mathfrak{a}=x_1 \vee G_i\mathfrak{a}$, and every prime formula $H_j\mathfrak{ab}$ by $\overline{\mathfrak{a}=x_1} \vee \overline{\mathfrak{b}=x_1} \vee Y_j \;\&\; \mathfrak{a}=x_1 \vee \overline{\mathfrak{b}=x_1}\, K_j\mathfrak{a}$ & & $\overline{\mathfrak{a}=x_1} \vee \mathfrak{b}=x_1 \vee L_j\mathfrak{b} \;\&\; \mathfrak{a}=x_1 \vee \mathfrak{b}=x_1 \vee H_j\mathfrak{ab}$. $X_i$ and $Y_j$ are propositional variables; $K_j$ and $L_j$ are monadic predicate variables ($i=1, \dots, p$; $j=1, \dots q$). Let $\Phi_i$ and $\Psi_j$ be an arbitrary assignment for $G_i$ and $H_j$ and let $\Omega$ be an arbitrary assignment for the individual variables of the matrix of $\mathfrak{A}$ in a domain $D$. The element $a$ of $D$ may be assigned to $x_1$ by $\Omega$. Let $\Delta_i$, $\Gamma_j$, $\Theta_j$, $\Lambda_j$ be assignments for $X_i$, $Y_j$, $K_j$ and $L_j$ such that $\Delta_i$ and $\Gamma_j$ are the values of $\Phi_i(a)$ and $\Psi_j(a, a)$, and such that $\Theta_j(c)$ and $\Lambda_j(c)$ always have the same value as $\Psi_j(c, a)$ and $\Psi_j(a, c)$. Any prime formula $G_i\mathfrak{a}$ or $H_j\mathfrak{a}\mathfrak{b}$ of $\mathfrak{A}$ then has the same value by $\Phi_i$, $\Psi_j$, $\Omega$ as the corresponding formula of $\mathfrak{B}$ has by $\Delta_i$, $\Gamma_j$, $\Theta_j$, $\Lambda_j$, $\Phi_i$, $\Psi_j$, $\Omega$.

On the other hand, let $\Delta_i$, $\Gamma_j$, $\Theta_j$, $\Lambda_j$, $\Phi_i$, $\Psi_j$, $\Omega$ be an arbitrary assignment for $X_i$, $Y_j$, $K_j$, $L_j$, $G_i$, $H_j$ and the individual variables of the matrix of $\mathfrak{B}$; let the element $a$ be assigned to $x_1$ by $\Omega$. We define propositional functions $\Phi_i'$ and $\Psi_j'$ suitable as assignments for $G_i$ and $H_j$. $\Phi_i'(a)$ has the value $\Delta_i$; otherwise, $\Phi_i'(c)$ always has the same value as $\Phi_i(c)$. $\Psi_j'(a, a)$ has the value $\Gamma_j$. $\Psi_j'(c, a)$ and $\Psi_j'(a, c)$ have the same value as $\Theta_j(c)$ and $\Lambda_j(c)$, if $c$ is different from $a$. If both $c_1$ and $c_2$ are different from $a$, the value of $\Psi_j'(c_1, c_2)$ is the same as that of $\Psi_j(c_1, c_2)$. Any prime formula of $\mathfrak{A}$ again has the same value by $\Phi_i'$, $\Psi_j'$, $\Omega$ as the corresponding formula of $\mathfrak{B}$ has by $\Delta_i$, $\Gamma_j$, $\Theta_j$, $\Lambda_j$, $\Phi_i$, $\Psi_j$, $\Omega$.

Therefore the wffs $\mathfrak{A}$ and $\mathfrak{B}$ are valid in the same domains.

In the following, $('\mathfrak{a})\mathfrak{A}(\mathfrak{a})$ may be an abbreviation for $(\mathfrak{a})(\mathfrak{a}=x_1 \vee \mathfrak{A}(\mathfrak{a}))$ and $(E'\mathfrak{a})\mathfrak{A}(\mathfrak{a})$ a similar one for $(E\mathfrak{a})(\overline{\mathfrak{a}=x_1} \,\&\, \mathfrak{A}(\mathfrak{a}))$. If a wff

$$(x_1)('x_2)\dots('x_m)(E'y_1)\dots(E'y_n)('z_1)\dots('z_s)\mathfrak{H}(x_2,\dots,x_m,y_1,\dots,y_n,z_1\dots z_s)$$

(where $\mathfrak{H}$ does not contain the variable $x_1$) is valid in a domain $D$ with at least two elements, then it is obvious that

$$(x_2)\dots(x_m)(Ey_1)\dots(Ey_n)(z_1)\dots(z_s)\mathfrak{H}(x_2,\dots,x_m,y_1,\dots,y_n,z_1,\dots z_s)$$

is valid in a domain $D_1$ which results from $D$ by excluding one element, and conversely.

We now transform $\mathfrak{B}$ in a manner such that it becomes a conjunction of wffs of the above kind.

$\mathfrak{B}$ has the prefix $(x_1)\dots(x_m)(Ey_1)\dots(Ey_n)(z_1)\dots(z_k)$ and a matrix $\mathfrak{C}(x_1, \dots, x_m, y_1, \dots, y_n, z_1, \dots, z_k)$. $\mathfrak{B}$ is changed into $\mathfrak{B}_1$ by replacing $\mathfrak{C}$ by $\mathfrak{C}_1$. $\mathfrak{C}_1$ is the conjunction of all possible wffs $\mathfrak{C}(x_1, \dots, x_m, y_1, \dots, y_n, \mathfrak{a}_1, \dots, \mathfrak{a}_k)$ where $\mathfrak{a}_1, \dots, \mathfrak{a}_k$ are variables from the set $x_1, z_1, \dots, z_k$.

$('z_1)\dots('z_k)\mathfrak{C}_1$ and $(z_1)\dots(z_k)\mathfrak{C}$ get the same value by any assignment in a domain which has at least two elements. $\mathfrak{C}_2$ results from $\mathfrak{C}_1$ by replacing every wff prime formula $x_1=x_1$ by $T$ and every prime formula $z_i=x_1$ or $x_1=z_i$ by $F$ and then by reduction of the

$S$-formula according to II, § 3. By this transformation, $\mathfrak{B}_1$ becomes $\mathfrak{B}_2$. $\mathfrak{B}_2$ is equivalent to $\mathfrak{B}_1$, since $('z_1) \dots ('z_k)$ preceeds $\mathfrak{C}_1$. Let $\mathfrak{D}(x_1, \dots, x_m, y_1, \dots, y_n)$ be $('z_1) \dots ('z_k)\mathfrak{C}_2(x_1, \dots, x_m, y_1, \dots, y_n, z_1, \dots, z_k)$. $\mathfrak{D}_1(x_1, \dots, x_m, y_1, \dots, y_n)$ is the disjunction of all wffs $\mathfrak{D}(x_1, \dots, x_m, \mathfrak{b}_1, \dots, \mathfrak{b}_n)$ where $\mathfrak{b}_1, \dots, \mathfrak{b}_n$ are variables from the set $x_1, y_1, \dots, y_n$. $(Ey_1) \dots (Ey_n)\mathfrak{D}(x_1, \dots, x_m, y_1, \dots, y_n)$ and $(E'y_1) \dots (E'y_n)\mathfrak{D}_1(x_1, \dots, x_m, y_1, \dots, y_n)$ get the same valuation by any assignment in a domain with at least two elements. $\mathfrak{D}_2$ results from $\mathfrak{D}_1$ by replacing every prime formula $x_1 = x_1$ by $T$ and every prime formula $y_i = x_1$ or $x_1 = y_i$ by $F$ and by subsequent reduction according to II, § 3. $(E'y_1) \dots \dots (E'y_n)\mathfrak{D}_1$ and $(E'y_1) \dots (E'y_n)\mathfrak{D}_2$ are equivalent. The last wff may be abbreviated by $\mathfrak{E}(x_1, \dots, x_m)$. Let $\mathfrak{E}_i(x_1, x_2, \dots, x_m)$ be one of the wffs $\mathfrak{E}(x_1, \mathfrak{c}_2, \dots, \mathfrak{c}_m)$ where $\mathfrak{c}_2, \dots, \mathfrak{c}_m$ are variables from the set $x_1, x_2, \dots, x_m$. Not every $\mathfrak{E}_i$, of course, contains all the variables $x_1, \dots, x_m$. It is to be understood that in the following formulas vacuous quantifiers are deleted. For domains having at least two elements, $(x_1) \dots (x_m)\mathfrak{E}(x_1, x_2, \dots, x_m)$ (and therefore $\mathfrak{B}$) get the same value by any assignment as the conjunction of all wffs $(x_1)('x_2) \dots ('x_m)\mathfrak{E}_i(x_1, x_2, \dots, x_m)$. $\mathfrak{E}_i'(x_1, x_2, \dots, x_m)$ results from $\mathfrak{E}_i(x_1, x_2, \dots, x_m)$ by replacing every prime formula $x_1 = x_1$ by $T$ and every prime formula $x_1 = x_i$ or $x_i = x_1$ $(i \neq 1)$ by $F$ and by subsequent reduction according to II, § 3. Every wff $(x_1)('x_2) \dots ('x_m)\mathfrak{E}_i(x_1, \dots, x_m)$ is equivalent to $(x_1)('x_2) \dots ('x_m)\mathfrak{E}_i'(x_1, \dots, x_m)$. Each of the last formulas can be given a prenex normal form with a prefix

$$(x_1)('x_2) \dots ('x_m)(E'y_1) \dots (E'y_n)('z_1) \dots ('z_r)$$

and a matrix

$$\mathfrak{C}_i(x_1, \dots, x_m, y_1, \dots y_n, z_1, \dots, z_r).$$

But $\mathfrak{C}_i$ does not contain the variable $x_1$; for all the prime formulas $x_1 = x_1$, $x_1 = x_i$, $x_i = x_1$, $y_i = x_1$, $x_1 = y_i$, $z_i = x_1$ and $x_1 = z_i$ have been eliminated. Nor does $x_1$ occur in other prime formulas; for regarding the construction of $\mathfrak{B}$, a wff $G_i x_1$ would only occur as part of $x_1 = x_1 \vee G_i x_1$. Likewise prime formulas $H_j \mathfrak{a} x_1$, $H_j x_1 \mathfrak{a}$, $K_j x_1$ and $L_j x_1$ would only occur as terms of a disjunction of which $x_1 = x_1$ is another term. All such prime formulas have disappeared with the elimination of $x_1 = x_1$.

Therefore $\mathfrak{B}$ is valid in a domain having at least two elements, if and only if all the wffs

$$(x_2) \dots (x_m)(Ey_1) \dots (Ey_n)(z_1) \dots (z_r)\mathfrak{C}_i(x_1, \dots, x_m, y_1, \dots, y_n, z_1 \dots z_r)$$

are valid in a domain which has one less element. The wffs $\mathfrak{C}_i$ contain propositional variables, but these variables can be eliminated according to II, § 3. The elimination means only that the number of the wffs above is multiplied by $2^g$, if $g$ is the number of the propositional variables.

By applying this reduction several times, we get the following result. *A wff $\mathfrak{A}$ with a prefix $(x_1) \dots (x_m)(Ey_1) \dots (Ey_n)(z_1) \dots (z_k)$ and without free individual variables is valid in a finite domain with at least $m+t$ elements ($t \geqslant 1$), if and only if a certain finite number of wffs $\mathfrak{B}_i$ with prefixes $(Ey_1) \dots (Ey_n)(z_1) \dots (z_{r_i})$, which can be constructed from $\mathfrak{A}$, are all valid in a domain with t elements. Here n has not increased while $r_i$ may be greater than k. But if $k=0$, all $r_i$ are* 0. *$\mathfrak{A}$ is valid in a denumerably infinite domain, if and only if all the wffs $\mathfrak{B}_i$ are valid in such a domain.*

If for the wffs $\mathfrak{B}_i$ the decision problem is solved, we get a solution of the problem for $\mathfrak{A}$ after having investigated the validity of $\mathfrak{A}$ in domains with 1, 2, ..., $m$ elements.

## 5. Solution for wffs having prefixes such that all the universal quantifiers precede all the existential ones

This case of the decision problem as well as the cases treated in § 2 and § 3 of this chapter were first solved by P. Bernays and M. Schönfinkel [1] for wffs not containing equality.

Let $(x_1) \dots (x_m)(Ey_1) \dots (Ey_n)\mathfrak{A}(x_1, \dots, x_m, y_1, \dots, y_n)$ be the wff. If a wff of this kind is valid in a domain $D$ with at least m elements, it is valid in any larger domain. Let $D_1$ be such a larger domain. If we have an arbitrary assignment $a_1, \dots, a_m, \Omega$ for the individual variables $x_1, \dots, x_m$ and for the predicate variables of $(Ey_1) \dots (Ey_n)\mathfrak{A}(x_1, \dots, x_m, y_1, \dots, y_n)$ in $D_1$, there is a subdomain $D_2$ of $D_1$ which has the same number of elements as $D$ and which contains the elements $a_1, \dots, a_m$. Let $\Omega'$ be the assignment for the predicate variables in $D_2$ consisting of those propositional functions over $D_2$ which coincide with the propositional functions of $\Omega$, so far as only elements of $D_2$ are concerned. $(Ey_1) \dots (Ey_n)\mathfrak{A}(a_1, \dots, a_m, y_1, \dots, y_n)$ is true in $D_2$ by $\Omega'$. There exist then elements $b_1, \dots, b_n$ of $D_2$ such that $\mathfrak{A}(a_1, \dots, a_m, b_1, \dots, b_n)$ is true in $D_2$ by $\Omega'$. Obviously $\mathfrak{A}(a_1, \dots, a_m, b_1, \dots, b_n)$ is true in $D_1$ by $\Omega$. Since $\Omega$ and $a_1, \dots, a_m$ were arbitrary,

$$(Ey_1) \dots (Ey_n)\mathfrak{A}(x_1, \dots, x_m, y_1, \dots, y_n)$$

is valid in $D_1$.

*The problem of universal validity for wffs having the prefix above can now be solved. A wff of this kind is universally valid if it is valid in domains with* 1, 2, ..., *m elements.*

*For the wffs which do not contain the sign of equality, validity in all domains can be determined by use of TII of V,* § 2. *We first ascertain whether the wff is valid in a domain with m elements. If it is, it is universally valid. If not, validity exists at most in domains with* 1, 2, ..., $m-1$ *elements, for which the validity can be determined in the usual way.*

*For the wffs which may contain the sign of equality, the solution of the form II of the decision problem can be found by making use of the theorem of* § 4, *by which the present case is reduced to the one treated in* § 3 *of this chapter.*

# VII

# FURTHER CLASSES OF PREFIXES FOR WHICH THE DECISION PROBLEM CAN BE SOLVED

## 1. Solution for wffs having prefixes containing only one existential quantifier

The wff has the form

$$(x_1) \dots (x_m)(Ey)(z_1) \dots (z_n)\mathfrak{A}(x_1, \dots, x_m, y, z_1, \dots, z_n).$$

This case of the decision problem, for wffs not containing equality, was first solved by W. Ackermann [1] for the form II of the decision problem and independently by Th. Skolem [3] for $m=0$ and the form I of the problem. The subcase $m=0$, $n=1$ had been treated before by P. Bernays and M. Schönfinkel [1].

This special case is contained in the case treated in § 2 of this chapter. But as the argumentations used here are much simpler than those used in § 2, a separate treatment may be justified. By force of the reduction theorem of § 4 of the preceding chapter, it is sufficient to give the solution for $m=0$, i.e. for wffs of the form $(Ex)(y_1) \dots (y_n)\mathfrak{B}(x, y_1, \dots, y_n)$.

Our treatment of the case is different from that given in the above cited papers inasmuch as we give a reduction of the problem to that for wffs with only monadic predicate variables. Here again, we restrict ourselves to the case where $\mathfrak{B}$ contains only dyadic predicate variables, namely $G_1, \dots, G_l$, from which the essence of the method is to be recognized.

Let $\mathfrak{C}(x, y_1, \dots, y_n)$ be the conjunction of all wffs $\mathfrak{B}(x, \mathfrak{a}_1, \dots, \mathfrak{a}_n)$ in which $\mathfrak{a}_1, \dots, \mathfrak{a}_n$ is a $n$-tuple selected from the set $(x, y_1, \dots, y_n)$. Further, let $\mathfrak{P}(x, y_1, \dots, y_n)$ be the disjunction of all wffs $x=y_p$ and $y_p=y_q$ $(p, q=1, \dots, n;\ p\neq q)$. If $(Ex)(y_1) \dots (y_n)\mathfrak{B}(x, y_1, \dots, y_n)$ is valid in a domain, $(Ex)(y_1) \dots (y_n)(\mathfrak{P}(x, y_1, \dots, y_n) \vee \mathfrak{C}(x, y_1, \dots, y_n))$ is valid in the same domain. If the last wff is valid in some domain, the first one is valid in the same domain, provided the domain has at least $n+1$ elements. This is easily seen by the construction of $\mathfrak{C}(x, y_1, ..., y_n)$.

In $\mathfrak{C}(x, y_1, ..., y_n)$, we replace the prime formulas $G_i xx$, $G_i xy_p$, $G_i y_p x$, $G_i y_p y_p$ and $G_i y_p y_q$ ($p \neq q$) by $H_i x$, $K_{ip} x$, $L_{ip} x$, $H_i y_p$, and $M_{ipq} x$. $\mathfrak{C}(x, y_1, ..., y_n)$ is thus transformed into $\mathfrak{D}(x, y_1, ..., y_n)$ which contains only the monadic predicate variables $H_i$, $K_{ip}$, $L_{ip}$ and $M_{ipq}$. Let $N_1$, $N_2$, $N_3$ be three other monadic predicate variables. We now consider the wff which has the prefix $(Ex)(y_1) ... (y_n)$ and the matrix of which is the disjunction of the terms $\mathfrak{P}(x, y_1, ..., y_n)$, $N_1 x \ \& \ \overline{N_2 y_1} \vee ... \vee \overline{N_2 y_n}$, $N_2 x \ \& \ \overline{N_3 y_1} \vee ... \vee \overline{N_3 y_n}$, $N_3 x \ \& \ \overline{N_1 y_1} \vee ... \vee \overline{N_1 y_n}$, $\overline{N_1 x} \ \& \ \overline{N_2 x} \ \& \ \overline{N_3 x}$, $N_1 x \ \& \ N_2 x$, $N_1 x \ \& \ N_3 x$, $N_2 x \ \& \ N_3 x$, and $\mathfrak{D}(x, y_1, ..., y_n)$. We shall abbreviate this wff by $\mathfrak{H}$, while the wff $(Ex)(y_1) ... (y_n)(\mathfrak{P}(x, y_1, ..., y_n) \vee \mathfrak{C}(x, y_1, ..., y_n))$ may be abbreviated by $\mathfrak{G}$.

We shall prove that the following relations exist between $\mathfrak{G}$ and $\mathfrak{H}$. If $\mathfrak{G}$ is valid in a domain, $\mathfrak{H}$ is valid in the same domain. If $\mathfrak{H}$ is valid in a denumerably infinite domain, $\mathfrak{G}$ is universally valid.

This suffices to solve the decision problem for the wffs $(Ex)(y_1) ... (y_n)\mathfrak{B}(x, y_1, ..., y_n)$ in the form II. *Since $\mathfrak{H}$ contains only monadic predicate variables, it can be determined in which domains it is valid. If it is valid in a denumerably infinite domain, $\mathfrak{G}$ is universally valid, and $(Ex)(y_1) ... (y_n)\mathfrak{B}(x, y_1, ..., y_n)$ is valid in any domain with the possible exception of domains with $1, 2, ..., n+1$ elements, for which the validity can be determined by the methods of I, § 2. If $\mathfrak{H}$ is not valid in a denumerably infinite domain, it is either not valid in any domain, in which case $\mathfrak{G}$ and $(Ex)(y_1) ... (y_n)\mathfrak{B}(x, y_1, ..., y_n)$ are not valid in any domain; or $\mathfrak{H}$ is valid only in a finite number of finite domains which can be determined, in which case $(Ex)(y_1) ... (y_n)$ $\mathfrak{B}(x, y_1, ..., y_n)$ is at most valid in these finite domains. Whether this is the case, can be determined by the methods of I, § 2.*

Now for the proof of above assertion. Let $\mathfrak{G}$ be valid in a domain $D$. Let $\Phi_i$, $\Theta_{ip}$, $\Lambda_{ip}$, $\Gamma_{ipq}$, $\Pi_1$, $\Pi_2$, $\Pi_3$ be arbitrary propositional functions over $D$, suitable as assignments for $H_i$, $K_{ip}$, $L_{ip}$, $M_{ipq}$, $N_1$, $N_2$ and $N_3$. If $\mathfrak{H}$ were false by this assignment, there would be functions $\varphi_1, ..., \varphi_n$, the domain and the range of which is $D$ such that for every element $a$ of $D$ $\varphi_i a = a$, $\varphi_p a = \varphi_q a$, ($p \neq q$) and

$\mathfrak{D}(a, \varphi_1 a, \ldots, \varphi_n a)$ are false, and such that $\overline{\Pi_1 a} \vee \overline{\Pi_2 a}$ & $\overline{\Pi_2 a} \vee \overline{\Pi_3 a}$ & & $\overline{\Pi_1 a} \vee \overline{\Pi_3 a}$, and one of the formulas $\Pi_1 a$ & $\Pi_2 \varphi_1 a$ & ... & $\Pi_2 \varphi_n a$, $\Pi_2 a$ & $\Pi_3 \varphi_1 a$ & ... & $\Pi_3 \varphi_n a$, $\Pi_3 a$ & $\Pi_1 \varphi_1 a$ & ... & $\Pi_1 \varphi_n a$, are true. We define propositional functions $\Psi_1 - \Psi_l$ over $D$. $\Psi_i(a, a)$ and $\Phi_i(a)$, $\Psi_i(a, \varphi_p a)$ and $\Theta_{ip}(a)$, $\Psi_i(\varphi_p a, a)$ and $\Lambda_{ip}(a)$, and $\Psi_i(\varphi_p a, \varphi_q a)$ and $\Gamma_{ipq}(a)$ have the same value; otherwise the definition of the functions $\Psi_i$ is arbitrary. Such a definition is consistent, since $a \neq \varphi_p a$, $\varphi_p a \neq \varphi_q a$, $(p \neq q)$ and as pairs $(a, \varphi_p a)$, $(\varphi_q b, b)$, and $(\varphi_r c, \varphi_s c)$ cannot be the same because of the stated properties of $\Pi_1$, $\Pi_2$, $\Pi_3$. In that case, $\mathfrak{P}(a, \varphi_1 a, \ldots, \varphi_n a) \vee \mathfrak{C}(a, \varphi_1 a, \ldots, \varphi_n a)$ would be false by $\Psi_1, \ldots, \Psi_l$, which contradicts our assumption that $\mathfrak{G}$ is valid in $D$. Therefore, $\mathfrak{H}$ is true by $\Phi_i$, $\Theta_{ip}$, $\Lambda_{ip}$, $\Gamma_{ipq}$, $\Pi_1$, $\Pi_2$, $\Pi_3$, and is valid in $D$, since the assignment was arbitrary.

Let $\mathfrak{H}$ be valid in the domain $D$ of the non-negative integers; let $D_1$ be an arbitrary domain. If $\mathfrak{G}$ were not valid in $D_1$, then there would be propositional functions $\Psi_1, \ldots, \Psi_l$ and ordinary functions $\varphi_1, \ldots, \varphi_n$ in $D_1$ such that $\mathfrak{P}(a, \varphi_1 a, \ldots, \varphi_n a)$ and $\mathfrak{C}(a, \varphi_1 a, \ldots, \varphi_n a)$ would be false for every $a$ of $D_1$ by $\Psi_1, \ldots, \Psi_l$. To every element $b$ of $D$ we let correspond in a unique way an element $\omega b$ of $D_1$. The element of $D_1$ corresponding to the element 0 of $D$ is some arbitrarily chosen, but fixed, element of $D_1$. If an element $b$ of $D$ is equal to $3na + 3(i-1) + k$ $(1 \leqslant i \leqslant n;\ 0 \leqslant k \leqslant 2)$, $\omega b$ is $\varphi_i \omega a$. We define monadic propositional functions $\Phi_i$, $\Theta_{ip}$, $\Lambda_{ip}$, $\Gamma_{ipq}$, $\Pi_1$, $\Pi_2$, $\Pi_3$ over $D$. $\Phi_i(b)$ has the same value as $\Psi_i(\omega b, \omega b)$ for every element $b$. $\Pi_i(b)$ is true or false depending upon whether $b$ results in the remainder $i-1$ by division through 3 or not. $\Theta_{ip}(b)$, $\Lambda_{ip}(b)$, $\Gamma_{ipq}(b)$ have the same value respectively as $\Psi_i(\omega b, \varphi_p \omega b)$, $\Psi_i(\varphi_p \omega b, \omega b)$, and $\Psi_i(\varphi_p \omega b, \varphi_q \omega b)$. Let $\chi_1, \ldots, \chi_n$ be the following functions in $D$. If $b+1$ produces the remainder $k$ by division through 3,

$$\chi_i(b) = 3nb + 3(i-1) + k.$$

Obviously, $\omega \chi_i(b) = \varphi_i \omega b$. For any element $b$ of $D$, $\mathfrak{C}(\omega b, \varphi_1 \omega b, \ldots, \varphi_n \omega b)$ is false by $\Psi_1, \ldots, \Psi_l$. $\mathfrak{D}(b, \chi_1 b, \ldots, \chi_n b)$ is false by $\Phi_i, \ldots, \Pi_3$, and the formula which results from the matrix of $\mathfrak{H}$ by replacing $x$ by $b$ and $y_1, \ldots, y_n$ by $\chi_1 b, \ldots, \chi_n b$ is also false. This would contradict the assumption that $\mathfrak{H}$ is valid in $D$; therefore, $\mathfrak{G}$ is valid in $D_1$.

## 2. Solution for wffs having prefixes containing only two existential quantifiers which are not separated by universal quantifiers

In this case, the wff has the form

$$(x_1) \dots (x_m)(Ey_1)(Ey_2)(z_1) \dots (z_n)\mathfrak{A}(x_1, \dots, x_m, y_1, y_2, z_1, \dots, z_n).$$

The solution of the decision problem was given independently by K. Gödel [2, 3], L. Kalmar [4], and K. Schütte [1, 2]. Gödel and Schütte give the solution for the form II of the problem, while Kalmar's solution is restricted to form I.

Taking into consideration the reduction theorem of § 4 of the preceding chapter, we see that it is sufficient to solve the problem for wffs of the form

$$(Ex_1)(Ex_2)(y_1) \dots (y_n)\mathfrak{A}(x_1, x_2, y_1, \dots, y_n).$$

The solution of form I of the decision problem is easier to obtain than the solution of form II we have given here. We restrict ourselves, as do the cited papers, to wffs which do not contain the equality sign.

The method we are following here is in a certain way similar to that used in § 1 of this chapter inasmuch as we shall reduce the problem to a similar one for the monadic predicate calculus simultaneously making use of some of Gödel's ideas. The idea of the proof can be fully grasped if we exhibit it for the case in which the wff in question contains only one dyadic predicate variable $G$ and only two universal quantifiers.

We therefore start from a wff

$$(Ex_1)(Ex_2)(y_1)(y_2)\mathfrak{A}(x_1, x_2, y_1, y_2)$$

which we shall designate by $\mathfrak{C}$. We construct a wff with only monadic predicate variables which stands in a certain relation to $\mathfrak{C}$. The monadic predicate variables occurring in it are $H, K_1, \dots, K_7, L_1, L_2, M_i$ $(i=0, \dots, 15)$ $N_i, P_i$ $(i=1, \dots, 7)$. $\Pi_i, \Pi_{i,k}$, etc. are used in the following to designate a disjunction of terms in which $i$, or $i$ and $k$, run through all possible values of certain indices. For instance, $\Pi_i L_i x$ means $L_1 x \vee L_2 x$; $\Pi_{i,j}(M_i x \,\&\, M_i y)$ means the disjunction of all terms $(M_i x \,\&\, M_j y)$ in which $i$ and $j$

may be independently any of the numbers 0, 1, ..., 15. In the same way $\Sigma_i$, $\Sigma_{i,k}$, etc. are used to designate certain conjunctions.

Let $\alpha$ be a function, the domain and range of which are the natural numbers 1, ..., 7, and which has the property that $\alpha(i, \alpha(j, k))$ and $\alpha(\alpha(j, k), i)$ are always different from $j$ and $k$. Such a function exists, as can be immediately shown (a domain with seven elements being the smallest domain in which such a function exists). We select a special function of this kind so that $\alpha$ always represents this function. The property of $\alpha$ stated above includes the case in which always $\alpha(i, k) \neq i$ and $\alpha(i, k) \neq k$. $\Delta_{kij} (k = 0, \ldots, 15;\ i, j = 1, 2)$ is a truth-value $T$ or $F$. If $k = \varepsilon_0 2^0 + \varepsilon_1 2^1 + \varepsilon_2 2^2 + \varepsilon_3 2^3$ $(\varepsilon_i = 0, 1)$, then $\Delta_{k11}$, $\Delta_{k12}$, $\Delta_{k21}$, and $\Delta_{k22}$ are $T$ or $F$ in case $\varepsilon_0$, $\varepsilon_1$, $\varepsilon_2$, $\varepsilon_3$ are respectively 0 or 1. $\delta$, $\gamma_1, \ldots, \gamma_5$ are functions, the domains and ranges of which is the set (0, 1, ..., 15). If $k = \varepsilon_0 2^0 + \varepsilon_1 2^1 + \varepsilon_2 2^2 + \varepsilon_3 2^3$ $(\varepsilon_i = 0, 1)$, then $\delta(k) = \varepsilon_3 2^0 + \varepsilon_2 2^1 + \varepsilon_1 2^2 + \varepsilon_0 2^3$. $\gamma_1, \ldots, \gamma_5$ are not further specified except that they satisfy the condition that $\Delta_{k11}$, $\Delta_{\gamma_1(k)11}$, and $\Delta_{\gamma_2(k)11}$; $\Delta_{k22}$, $\Delta_{\gamma_3(k)11}$, and $\Delta_{\gamma_4(k)11}$; $\Delta_{\gamma_1(k)22}$, $\Delta_{\gamma_3(k)22}$, and $\Delta_{\gamma_5(k)11}$; $\Delta_{\gamma_2(k)22}$, $\Delta_{\gamma_4(k)22}$, and $\Delta_{\gamma_5(k)22}$ have the same truth-values. Furthermore, if $\Delta_{k11}$, $\Delta_{k12}$, $\Delta_{k21}$, and $\Delta_{k22}$ have the same truth-value, then $\gamma_1(k) = \gamma_3(k)$, and $\gamma_2(k) = \gamma_4(k)$.

We introduce several *abbreviations*. Let $\mathfrak{E}(i)$ be the formula which results from $\mathfrak{A}(x_1, x_2, y_1, y_2)$ by replacing $Gx_1x_1$, $Gx_1x_2$, $Gx_2x_1$, $Gx_2x_2$, $Gx_1y_1$, $Gy_1x_1$, $Gy_1y_1$, $Gx_1y_2$, $Gy_2x_1$, $Gy_2y_2$, $Gx_2y_1$, $Gy_1x_2$, $Gx_2y_2$, $Gy_2x_2$, $Gy_1y_2$, and $Gy_2y_1$ respectively, by $\Delta_{i11}$, $\Delta_{i12}$, $\Delta_{i21}$, $\Delta_{i22}$, $\Delta_{\gamma_1(i)12}$, $\Delta_{\gamma_1(i)21}$, $\Delta_{\gamma_1(i)22}$, $\Delta_{\gamma_2(i)12}$, $\Delta_{\gamma_2(i)21}$, $\Delta_{\gamma_2(i)22}$, $\Delta_{\gamma_3(i)12}$, $\Delta_{\gamma_3(i)21}$, $\Delta_{\gamma_4(i)12}$, $\Delta_{\gamma_4(i)21}$, $\Delta_{\gamma_5(i)12}$, and $\Delta_{\gamma_5(i)21}$.

$\mathfrak{K}_{ijk}(x_1, x_2, y_1, y_2)$ is an abbreviation for the disjunction of the formulas $\overline{L_1y_1}$, $\overline{L_2y_2}$, $\overline{K_ix_1}$, $\overline{K_jx_2}$, $\overline{K_{\alpha(i,j)}y_1}$, $\overline{K_{\alpha(i,j)}y_2}$, $\overline{M_ky_1}$, $\overline{M_ky_2}$, $\overline{N_iy_1}$, $\overline{N_iy_2}$, $\overline{P_jy_1}$, $\overline{P_jy_2}$, $\Delta_{k11} \leftrightarrow \overline{Hx_1}$, $\Delta_{k22} \leftrightarrow \overline{Hx_2}$, $\Delta_{\gamma_1(k)22} \leftrightarrow \overline{Hy_1}$, $\Delta_{\gamma_2(k)22} \leftrightarrow \overline{Hy_2}$, and $x_1 = x_2 \mathbin{\&} (\Delta_{k11} \leftrightarrow \overline{\Delta_{k12}}) \vee (\Delta_{k12} \leftrightarrow \overline{\Delta_{k21}})$.

$\mathfrak{R}_{ijk}(x_1, x_2, y_1, y_2)$ stands for the disjunction of the formulas

$$(z_1)(z_2)\mathfrak{K}_{ji\delta(k)}(x_2, x_1, z_1, z_2),\quad (z_1)(z_2)\mathfrak{K}_{i\alpha(i,j)\gamma_1(k)}(x_1, y_1, z_1, z_2),$$
$$(z_1)(z_2)\mathfrak{K}_{i\alpha(i,j)\gamma_2(k)}(x_1, y_2, z_1, z_2),\quad (z_1)(z_2)\mathfrak{K}_{j\alpha(i,j)\gamma_3(k)}(x_2, y_1, z_1, z_2),$$
$$(z_1)(z_2)\mathfrak{K}_{j\alpha(i,j)\gamma_4(k)}(x_2, y_2, z_1, z_2), \text{ and } (z_1)(z_2)\mathfrak{K}_{\alpha(i,j)\alpha(i,j)\gamma_5(k)}(y_1, y_2, z_1, z_2).$$

Let $\mathfrak{D}$ be the disjunction of the formulas $(Ex)(L_1x \mathbin{\&} L_2x)$,

$\Pi_i(Ex)(M_ix \,\&\, \mathfrak{E}(i))$, $\Pi_{i\neq j}\,(Ex)\overline{(M_ix \,\&\, M_jx)}$, $\Pi_{i\neq j}\,(Ex)(N_ix \,\&\, N_jx)$, $\Pi_{i\neq j}\,(Ex)(P_ix \,\&\, P_jx)$, $(Ex)\overline{(K_1x \,\&\, \dots \,\&\, K_7x)}$, $\Pi_{i\neq j}\,(Ex)(K_ix \,\&\, K_jx)$, $(Ex_1)(Ex_2)(y_1)(y_2)\,\Sigma_{ijk}\,\mathfrak{K}_{ijk}(x_1, x_2, y_1, y_2)$, and

$$(Ex_1)(Ex_2)(Ey_1)(Ey_2)\,\Pi_{ijk}\,(\overline{\mathfrak{K}_{ijk}(x_1, x_2, y_1, y_2)} \,\&\, \mathfrak{N}_{ijk}(x_1, x_2, y_1, y_2)).$$

$\mathfrak{D}$ is an $S$-formula which contains the truth-values $T$ and $F$.

There exist the following (I and II) relations between $\mathfrak{C}$ and $\mathfrak{D}$.

I. If $\mathfrak{D}$ is valid in a denumerably infinite domain for arbitrary functions $\gamma_1, \dots, \gamma_5$, $\mathfrak{C}$ is universally valid.

Let $D$ be a domain in which $\mathfrak{C}$ be false by the assignment $\Phi$ for $G$. Then there exist functions $\varphi_1$ and $\varphi_2$ over $D$, the values of which are elements of $D$ such that for all $a$ and $b$ of $D$, $\mathfrak{A}(a, b, \varphi_1(a,b), \varphi_2(a, b))$ is false by $\Phi$.

We are now going to construct a denumerably infinite domain $D'$, the elements of which are non-negative integers. 0 is an element of $D'$. If $a'$ and $b'$ are elements of $D$, so are $\chi_1(a', b')$ and $\chi_2(a', b')$. ($\chi_1(a', b') = 2^{a'+1}(2b'+1)$; $\chi_2(a', b') = 2^{a'+1}(2b'+1)+1$). The elements generated from 0 by successive applications of $\chi_1$ and $\chi_2$ are the only elements of $D'$. Elements of $D'$ will be usually designated by $a', b', c', \dots$, elements of $D$ by $a, b, c, \dots$. We suppose the ordered pairs $(a, b)$ of elements of $D$ to be enumerated in some way. We introduce the expression: the first ordered pair of $D$ equivalent to an ordered pair $(c, d)$ of $D$. By this we understand the first ordered pair $(a, b)$ of $D$ such that $\Phi(a, a)$ and $\Phi(c, c)$, $\Phi(a, b)$ and $\Phi(c, d)$, $\Phi(b, a)$ and $\Phi(d, c)$, $\Phi(b, b)$ and $\Phi(d, d)$ have the same truth-value and such that $a = b$ if the values of $\Phi(c, c)$, $\Phi(c, d)$, $\Phi(d, c)$, and $\Phi(d\ d)$ are the same.

To every ordered pair $(a', b')$ of elements of $D'$, we let correspond an ordered pair $(a, b)$ of elements of $D$, which is defined by recursion. $a_0$ may be an arbitrary, but nevertheless a fixed element of $D$. The pair corresponding to $(0, 0)$ is the first pair equivalent to $(a_0, a_0)$. The pairs corresponding to $(a', \chi_1(a', b'))$, $(b', \chi_1(a', b'))$, $(\chi_1(a', b'), \chi_1(a', b'))$, $(a', \chi_2(a', b'))$, $(b', \chi_2(a', b'))$, $(\chi_2(a', b'), \chi_2(a', b'))$ $(\chi_1(a', b'), \chi_2(a', b'))$ are the first pairs equivalent to $(a, \varphi_1(a, b))$, $(b, \varphi_1(a, b))$, $(\varphi_1(a, b), \varphi_1(a, b))$, $(a, \varphi_2(a, b))$, $(b, \varphi_2(a, b))$, $(\varphi_2(a, b), \varphi_2(a, b))$, $(\varphi_1(a, b), \varphi_2(a, b))$, if $(a, b)$ corresponds to $(a', b')$. Otherwise, if

$c' < d'$, the pair corresponding to $(c', d')$ is the first pair equivalent to $(c, d)$ if $(c, c)$ corresponds to $(c', c')$ and $(d, d)$ to $(d', d')$. If $c' > d'$, the pair corresponding to $(c', d')$ is the first pair equivalent to $(c, d)$ if $(d, c)$ corresponds to $(d', c')$.

We now define monadic propositional functions $\Lambda$, $\Theta_i$, $Y_i$, $\Xi_i$ $(i = 1, \ldots, 7)$, and $\Psi_1$, $\Psi_2$, $\Gamma_i$ $(i = 0, \ldots, 15)$, over $D'$. $\Psi_1\chi_1(a', b')$ and $\Psi_2\chi_2(a', b')$ are true; otherwise $\Psi_1$ and $\Psi_2$ are false. $\Theta_1(0)$ is true; $Y_i(0)$ and $\Xi_i(0)$ are false. If $\Theta_i(a')$ and $\Theta_j(b')$ are true, $\Theta_{\alpha(i,j)}\chi_1(a', b')$, $\Theta_{\alpha(i,j)}\chi_2(a', b')$, $Y_i\chi_1(a', b')$, $Y_i\chi_2(a', b')$, $\Xi_j\chi_1(a', b')$, and $\Xi_j\chi_2(a', b')$ are true. If $i \neq j$ and if $\Theta_i(a')$ $(Y_i(a'), \Xi_i(a'))$ is true, then $\Theta_j(a')$ $(Y_j(a'), \Xi_j(a'))$ is false. $\Lambda(a')$ has the same value as $\Phi(a, a)$ if $(a, a)$ corresponds to $(a', a')$. To every ordered pair $(a', b')$ with the corresponding ordered pair $(a, b)$ we assign that number $k$ $(k = 0, \ldots$ $\ldots, 15)$ for which $\Delta_{k11}$, $\Delta_{k12}$, $\Delta_{k21}$, and $\Delta_{k22}$ are the values respectively of $\Phi(a, a)$, $\Phi(a, b)$, $\Phi(b, a)$, and $\Phi(b, b)$.

$\Gamma_k\chi_1(a', b')$ and $\Gamma_k\chi_2(a', b')$ are true if $k$ is assigned to $(a', b')$. In all other cases $\Gamma_k(a')$ is false.

We define functions $\gamma_1, \ldots, \gamma_5$ over the set $(0, \ldots, 15)$. If there is a pair $(a', b')$ such that $k$ is assigned to it, and if $i_1$, $i_2$, $i_3$, $i_4$, $i_5$ are the numbers assigned to $(a', \chi_1(a', b'))$, $(a', \chi_2(a', b'))$, $(b', \chi_1(a', b')$, $(b', \chi_2(a', b'))$, $(\chi_1(a', b')$, $\chi_2(a', b'))$, then $\gamma_1(k) = i_1$, $\gamma_2(k) = i_2, \ldots$, $\gamma_5(k) = i_5$. This definition is independent of the special pair $(a', b')$; for if $k$ is assigned to $(a', b')$ and to $(c', d')$, the ordered pairs of $D$ corresponding to $(a', b')$ and to $(c', d')$ are the same, and so are the pairs corresponding to $(a', \chi_1(a', b'))$ and $(c', \chi_1(c', d'))$, etc. On account of the definition of the corresponding pairs, $\gamma_1, \ldots, \gamma_5$ fulfil the conditions imposed on such functions occurring in $\mathfrak{D}$. In so far as the values of $\gamma_1, \ldots, \gamma_5$ are not thereby determined, they are arbitrary.

If $\Lambda$, $\Theta_i$, $Y_i$, $\Xi_i$, $\Psi_1$, $\Psi_2$, $\Gamma_i$ are assigned to $H$, $K_i$, $N_i$, $P_i$, $L_1$, $L_2$, $M_i$, and if the functions $\gamma_1, \ldots, \gamma_5$ are defined in the way just described, $\mathfrak{D}$ gets the value $F$.

We have to show that every disjunction term of $\mathfrak{D}$ is false by this assignment. If $\Gamma_i(a')$ is true, there are elements $c'$ and $b'$ such that $a' = \chi_s(b', c')$ and such that $i$ is assigned to $(b', c')$. If $(b, c)$ is the pair corresponding to $(b', c')$, then $\mathfrak{A}(b, c, \varphi_1(b, c), \varphi_2(b, c))$ is false by the assignment $\Phi$ for $G$. $\mathfrak{E}(i)$ results from $\mathfrak{A}(b, c, \varphi_1(b, c), \varphi_2(b, c))$ by replacing every prime formula $\Phi\mathfrak{a}\mathfrak{b}$ by a certain $\Delta_{kpq}$. Each such $\Phi\mathfrak{a}\mathfrak{b}$ and the pertaining $\Delta_{kpq}$ have the same truth-value; this immediately results from the definition of $\gamma_1, \ldots, \gamma_5$ and the definition of the corresponding pairs. Since $\mathfrak{E}(i)$ is false, $\Pi_i\,(Ex)(\Gamma_i x \;\&\; \mathfrak{E}(i))$ is false. $(Ex)\,(\Psi_1 x \;\&\; \Psi_2 x)$ is false according to the definition of $\Psi_i$.

$\Pi_{i \neq j}\,(Ex)(\Gamma_i x \;\&\; \Gamma_j x)$, $(Ex)(\overline{\Theta_1 x} \;\&\; \ldots \;\&\; \overline{\Theta_7 x})$, $\Pi_{i \neq j}\,(Ex)(Y_i x \;\&\; Y_j x)$, $\Pi_{i \neq j}\,(Ex)(\Xi_i x \;\&\; \Xi_j x)$, and $\Pi_{i \neq j}\,(Ex)(\Theta_i x \;\&\; \Theta_j x)$ are false as well with respect to the definitions of $\Gamma_i$, $Y_i$, $\Xi_i$ and $\Theta_i$. $\mathfrak{K}_{ijk}(a', b', \chi_1(a' b'), \chi_2(a', b'))$ is false by our assignment if $\Gamma_k \chi_1(a', b')$, $\Theta_i(a')$, and $\Theta_j(b')$ are true. Therefore, $(Ex_1)(Ex_2)(y_1)(y_2)\;\Sigma_{ikj}\;\mathfrak{K}_{ijk}(x_1, x_2, y_1, y_2)$ is false.

If $\mathfrak{K}_{ijk}(a', b', c', d')$ is false by our assignment, $\Gamma_k(c')$, $\Gamma_k(d')$, $\Theta_i(a')$, $\Theta_j(b')$, $Y_i(c')$, $Y_i(d')$, $\Xi_j(c')$, $\Xi_j(d')$, $\Psi_1(c')$, $\Psi_2(d')$, $\Theta_{\alpha(i,j)}(c')$, and $\Theta_{\alpha)i,j)}(d')$ are true. There are then elements $e'$ and $f'$ such that $c' = \chi_1(e', f')$, and such that $\Theta_i(e')$, $\Theta_j(f')$ are true. Let $g'$ be $\chi_2(e', f')$; then $\mathfrak{K}_{ijk}(a', b', c', g')$ is false too. Furthermore, each of the formulas

$$\mathfrak{K}_{ji\delta(k)}(b', a', \chi_1(f', e'), \chi_2(f', e')), \qquad \mathfrak{K}_{i\alpha(i,j)\gamma_1(k)}(a', c', \chi_1(e', c'), \chi_2(e', c')),$$
$$\mathfrak{K}_{i\alpha(i,j)\gamma_2(k)}(a', d', \chi_1(e', g'), \chi_2(e', g')), \quad \mathfrak{K}_{j\alpha(i,j)\gamma_3(k)}(b', c', \chi_1(f', c'), \chi_2(f', c')),$$
$$\mathfrak{K}_{j\alpha(i,j)\gamma_4(k)}(b', d', \chi_1(f', g'), \chi_2(f', g')), \text{and}\ \mathfrak{K}_{\alpha(i,j)\alpha(i,j)\gamma_5(k)}(c', d', \chi_1(c', g'), \chi_2(c', g'))$$

is false too; i.e. $\mathfrak{N}_{ijk}(a', b', c', d')$ is false.

This means that

$$(Ex_1)(Ex_2)(Ey_1)(Ey_2)\;\Pi_{ijk}\;(\overline{\mathfrak{K}_{ijk}(x_1, x_2, y_1, y_2) \;\&\; \mathfrak{N}_{ijk}(x_1, x_2, y_1, y_2)})$$

is false. As all the disjunction terms of $\mathfrak{D}$ are false by our assignment, so is $\mathfrak{D}$.

I has now been proved, for we have shown that $\mathfrak{D}$ cannot be valid in a denumerably infinite domain for arbitrary functions $\gamma_1, \ldots, \gamma_5$ if $\mathfrak{C}$ is not valid in all domains.

II. If $\mathfrak{C}$ is valid in a finite domain with $p^2$ elements, $\mathfrak{D}$ is valid in a domain with $p$ elements for arbitrary functions $\gamma_1, \ldots, \gamma_5$.

We again prove this in an indirect way. $D_1$ may be a domain with $p$ elements. There may exist functions $\gamma_1, \ldots, \gamma_5$ and an assignment $\Lambda$, $\Theta_i$, $Y_i$, $\Xi_i$, $\Psi_1$, $\Psi_2$, $\Gamma_i$ for $H$, $K_i$, $N_i$, $P_i$, $L_1$, $L_2$, $M_i$ such that $\mathfrak{D}$ is false by this assignment. For every element of $D_1$ there is then just one $i$ such that $\Theta_i(a)$ is true. $\Psi_1$ and $\Psi_2$, $\Gamma_i$ and $\Gamma_j$,

$Y_i$ and $Y_j$, and $\Xi_i$ and $\Xi_j$ are not true for the same element if $i \neq j$. The whole assignment may be designated by $\Omega$.

The elements of $D_1$ may be the numbers 1, 2, ..., $p$. Let $D_2$ be a domain, the elements of which are the numbers 1, 2, ..., $p^2$. Each element $a$ of $D_2$ has the form $b \cdot p + \varrho(a)$ $(0 \leqslant b \leqslant p-1;$ $1 \leqslant \varrho(a) \leqslant p)$, so that $b+1$ and $\varrho(a)$ are elements of $D_1$. We define a dyadic propositional function $\Phi$ over $D_2$.

$\alpha$) If $\varrho(a) = \varrho(b)$, $\Phi(a, b)$ has the same value as $\Lambda(\varrho(a))$.

$\beta$) If there is an $i$, $j$, $k$ such that $\mathfrak{R}_{ijk}(\varrho(a), \varrho(b), \varrho(c), \varrho(d))$ is false and if $c = (\varrho(a)-1)p + \varrho(c)$ and $d = (\varrho(a)-1)p + \varrho(d)$, then the values of 1) $\Phi(a, c)$ and $\Delta_{\gamma_1(k)12}$, 2) $\Phi(c, a)$ and $\Delta_{\gamma_1(k)21}$, 3) $\Phi(a, d)$ and $\Delta_{\gamma_2(k)12}$, 4) $\Phi(d, a)$ and $\Delta_{\gamma_2(k)21}$, 5) $\Phi(b, c)$ and $\Delta_{\gamma_3(k)12}$, 6) $\Phi(c, b)$ and $\Delta_{\gamma_3(k)21}$, 7) $\Phi(b, d)$ and $\Delta_{\gamma_4(k)12}$, 8) $\Phi(d, b)$ and $\Delta_{\gamma_4(k)21}$, 9) $\Phi(c, d)$ and $\Delta_{\gamma_5(k)12}$, 10) $\Phi(d, c)$ and $\Delta_{\gamma_5(k)21}$ are the same.

$\gamma$) If $(a, b)$ is a pair of elements of $D_2$ for which $\Phi(a, b)$ is not defined by $\beta$) and if $\varrho(a) < \varrho(b)$, then there are indices $i, j, k$ and elements $c$ and $d$ such that $\mathfrak{R}_{ijk}(\varrho(a), \varrho(b), \varrho(c), \varrho(d))$ is false by $\Omega$ and such that $c = (\varrho(a)-1)p + \varrho(c)$ and $d = (\varrho(a)-1)p + \varrho(d)$. For each such pair we select such an $i$, $j$, $k$, $c$, $d$; $\Phi(a, b)$ and $\Phi(b, a)$ then have the values $\Delta_{k12}$ and $\Delta_{k21}$.

We must show that this definition of $\Phi$ is consistent, i.e. that the value of $\Phi$ for an ordered pair is uniquely determined. If $\mathfrak{R}_{ijk}(\varrho(a), \varrho(b), \varrho(c), \varrho(d))$ is false by $\Omega$, then $\Theta_i\varrho(a)$, $\Theta_j\varrho(b)$, $\Theta_{\alpha(i,j)}\varrho(c)$, $\Theta_{\alpha(i,j)}\varrho(d)$, $\Psi_1(\varrho(c))$, and $\Psi_2\varrho(d)$ are true. As $\alpha(i, j) \neq i, j$ and because of the properties of $\Psi_1$ and $\Psi_2$, $\varrho(a) \neq \varrho(c)$, $\varrho(a) \neq \varrho(d)$, $\varrho(b) \neq \varrho(c)$, $\varrho(b) \neq \varrho(d)$, and $\varrho(c) \neq \varrho(d)$. $\alpha$) and $\beta$) therefore are not contradictory, since they relate to different pairs.

By each of the definitions $\beta$1), ..., $\beta$10) by itself $\Phi$ is uniquely determined, since for every element $\varrho(c)$ and $\varrho(d)$ there is only one $k$ such that $\Gamma_k\varrho(c)$ and $\Gamma_k(\varrho(d))$ are true. It remains to show that definitions $\beta m$) and $\beta n$) are not contradictory if $m \neq n$.

If the value of $\Phi(e, f)$ is determined by $\beta$1), ..., $\beta$10), and if $\Theta_i\varrho(e)$ and $\Theta_j\varrho(f)$ are true, the following relations exist:

$\beta_1$) $j = \alpha(i, r_1)$; $\Psi_1\varrho(f)$ (i.e. $\Psi_1\varrho(f)$ is true), $\beta$2) $i = \alpha(j, r_2)$; $\Psi_1\varrho(e)$, $\beta$3) $j = \alpha(i, r_3)$; $\Psi_2\varrho(f)$, $\beta$4) $i = \alpha(j, r_4)$; $\Psi_2\varrho(e)$, $\beta$5) $j = \alpha(r_5, i)$; $\Psi_1\varrho(f)$,

$\beta 6)$ $i=\alpha(r_6, j)$; $\Psi_1\varrho(e)$, $\beta 7)$ $j=\alpha(r_7, i)$; $\Psi_2\varrho(f)$, $\beta 8)$ $i=\alpha(r_8, j)$; $\Psi_2\varrho(e)$, $\beta 9)$ $i=j$; $\Psi_1\varrho(e)$; $\Psi_2\varrho(f)$, $\beta 10)$ $i=j$; $\Psi_1\varrho(f)$; $\Psi_2\varrho(e)$.

Since $\Psi_1$ and $\Psi_2$ are not true for the same element and since we always have $\alpha(s, t) \neq s, t$; $\alpha(\alpha(s, t), q) \neq s, t$, and $\alpha(q, \alpha(s, t)) \neq s, t$, only the definitions $\beta 1)$ and $\beta 5)$, $\beta 2)$ and $\beta 6)$, $\beta 3)$ and $\beta 7)$, and $\beta 4)$ and $\beta 8)$ may apply to the same ordered pair. If $\beta 1)$ and $\beta 5)$ give a definition for the same $\Phi(e, f)$, then there are indices $i, j, k$ and elements $g, d, h, c$ such that $\mathfrak{R}_{ijk}(\varrho e, \varrho g, \varrho f, \varrho d)$ and $\mathfrak{R}_{ijk}(\varrho h, \varrho e, \varrho f, \varrho c)$ are false by $\Omega$, and such that $f=(\varrho e-1)p+\varrho f$ and $f=(\varrho h-1)p+\varrho f$; then $\varrho(e)=\varrho(h)$, $\Delta_{k11} \leftrightarrow \Delta_{k12}$, $\Delta_{k12} \leftrightarrow \Delta_{k21}$, $\Delta_{k21} \leftrightarrow \Delta_{k22}$ and $\gamma_1(k)=\gamma_3(k)$ and $\gamma_2(k)=\gamma_4(k)$. According to $\beta 1)$, the value of $\Phi(e, f)$ is $\Delta_{\gamma_1(k)12}$ and according to $\beta 5)$, $\Delta_{\gamma_3(k)12}$; but this is the same value. In a similar way, it is shown that $\beta 2)$ and $\beta 6)$, $\beta 3)$ and $\beta 7)$, and $\beta 4)$ and $\beta 8)$ are consistent if they apply to the same ordered pair.

We now show that $(Ex_1)(Ex_2)(y_1)(y_2)\mathfrak{A}(x_1, x_2, y_1, y_2)$ is false in $D_2$ by the assignment $\Phi$ for G. Let $(a, b)$ be an ordered pair of elements of $D_2$. To prove that to such a pair there always exist elements $c$ and $d$ such that $\mathfrak{A}(a, b, c, d)$ is false by $\Phi$, we distinguish several cases.

1) $\varrho(a)=\varrho(b)$.

Because $\mathfrak{D}$ is false in $D_1$ by $\Omega$, there are indices $i, j, k$ and elements $c$ and $d$ of $D_2$ such that $\mathfrak{R}_{ijk}(\varrho a, \varrho b, \varrho c, \varrho d)$ is false by $\Omega$ and such that $c=(\varrho a-1)p+\varrho c$, $d=(\varrho a-1)p+\varrho d$. Since $\varrho a=\varrho b$, according to the definition of $\mathfrak{R}$ $\Delta_{k11}$, $\Delta_{k12}$, $\Delta_{k21}$, and $\Delta_{k22}$ are all the same truth-values and this is the value of $\Lambda(\varrho a)$. According to the definition of $\Phi$, each of the prime formulas of $\mathfrak{A}(a, b, c, d)$ with the assignment $\Phi$ for $G$ has the value of the corresponding formula $\Delta_{rst}$ of $\mathfrak{E}(k)$. Since $\Gamma_k(\varrho c)$ is true and since $\Pi_i\ (Ex)(\Gamma_i x \ \&\ \mathfrak{E}(i))$ is false, $\mathfrak{E}(k)$ is false as is also $\mathfrak{A}(a, b, c, d)$ by $\Phi$.

2) Let $\varrho(a)<\varrho(b)$ and $\Phi(a, b)$ be defined according to $\gamma$). Then there are an $i, j, k$ and elements $c$ and $d$ such that $\mathfrak{R}_{ijk}(\varrho a, \varrho b, \varrho c, \varrho d)$ is false, and such that $c=(\varrho a-1)p+\varrho c$, $d=(\varrho a-1)p+\varrho d$, $\Phi(a,b) \leftrightarrow \Delta_{k12}$, and $\Phi(b, a) \leftrightarrow \Delta_{k21}$. By the definition of $\mathfrak{R}$ and $\Phi$, $\mathfrak{E}(k)$ and $\mathfrak{A}(a, b, c, d)$ by $\Phi$ have the same value, since each $\Phi\mathfrak{a}\mathfrak{b}$ has the corresponding formula $\Delta_{rst}$ of $\mathfrak{E}(k)$ as value. Since $\mathfrak{E}(k)$ is false, $\mathfrak{A}(a, b, c, d)$ is false by $\Phi$.

3) Let $\varrho a > \varrho b$ and $\Phi(a, b)$ be defined according to $\gamma$).

Then there are an $i, j, k$ and elements $c$ and $d$ such that $\mathfrak{K}_{ijk}(\varrho b, \varrho a, \varrho c, \varrho d)$ is false and such that $\Phi(b, a)$ and $\Phi(a, b)$ have the values $\Delta_{k12}$ and $\Delta_{k21}$. Then $\mathfrak{N}_{ijk}(\varrho b, \varrho a, \varrho c, \varrho d)$ is false too; that is, there are elements $e$ and $f$ such that $e = (\varrho a - 1)p + \varrho e$, $f = (\varrho a - 1)p + \varrho f$, and such that $\mathfrak{K}_{ji\delta(k)}(\varrho a, \varrho b, \varrho e, \varrho f)$ is false by $\Omega$. $\mathfrak{A}(a, b, e, f)$ then has the same value as $\mathfrak{E}(\delta(k))$; i.e. it is false by $\Phi$.

4) Let $\Phi(a, b)$ be defined according to $\beta 1$).

Then $b = (\varrho a - 1)p + \varrho b$ and there are an $i, j, k$ and elements $c, d$ such that $\mathfrak{K}_{ijk}(\varrho a, \varrho c, \varrho b, \varrho d)$ is false by $\Omega$. Since $\mathfrak{N}_{ijk}(\varrho a, \varrho c, \varrho b, \varrho d)$ is false also, there are elements $e$ and $f$ such that $e = (\varrho a - 1)p + \varrho e$, $f = (\varrho a - 1)p + \varrho f$, and such that $\mathfrak{K}_{i\alpha(i,j)\gamma_1(k)}(\varrho a, \varrho b, \varrho e, \varrho f)$ is false by $\Omega$. As a result of the definition of $\Phi$, $\mathfrak{A}(a, b, e, f)$ by $\Phi$, and $\mathfrak{E}(\gamma_1(k))$ have the same value; i.e. $\mathfrak{A}(a, b, e, f)$ is false by $\Phi$.

5) Let $\Phi(a, b)$ be determined by $\beta 2$). Then some formula of the form $\mathfrak{K}_{ijk}(\varrho b, \varrho c, \varrho a, \varrho d)$ is false by $\Omega$, and so are $\mathfrak{N}_{ijk}(\varrho b, \varrho c, \varrho a, \varrho d)$, some formula of the form $\mathfrak{K}_{i\alpha(i,j)\gamma_1(k)}(\varrho b, \varrho a, \varrho e, \varrho f)$, $\mathfrak{N}_{i\alpha(i,j)\gamma_1(k)}(\varrho b, \varrho a, \varrho e, \varrho f)$ and a formula of the form $\mathfrak{K}_{\alpha(i,j)i\delta\gamma_1(k)}(\varrho a, \varrho b, \varrho g, \varrho h)$ where $g = (\varrho a - 1)p + \varrho g$, $h = (\varrho a - 1)p + \varrho h$. $\mathfrak{A}(a, b, g, h)$ is false by $\Phi$ because $\mathfrak{E}(\delta\gamma_1(k))$ is false.

6) If $\Phi(a, b)$ is defined according to $\beta 3$)—$\beta 10$), the argumentation is similar.

Thus II has been proved.

*The decision problem for wffs* $\mathfrak{C}$ *is now solved in the form II. Since* $\mathfrak{D}$ *contains only monadic predicate variables and since there are only a finite number of functions* $\gamma_1, \ldots, \gamma_5$, *it can be decided whether* $\mathfrak{D}$ *is valid in a denumerably infinite domain for arbitrary functions* $\gamma_1, \ldots, \gamma_5$. (The truth-values $\Delta_{ikj}$ occurring in $\mathfrak{D}$ are only a convenient means of describing the structure of $\mathfrak{D}$ and can be eliminated). *If it is valid in a denumerably infinite domain,* $\mathfrak{C}$ *is universally valid. Otherwise, we find functions* $\gamma_1, \ldots, \gamma_5$ *such that* $\mathfrak{D}$ *is not valid in a denumerably infinite domain; then we can find a finite domain in which this* $\mathfrak{D}$ *is not valid and the smallest such domain with* $k$ *elements. Then* $\mathfrak{C}$ *is not valid in domains with* $k^2$ *or more elements. Whether* $\mathfrak{C}$ *is valid in the domains with* $1, 2, \ldots, k^2 - 1$ *elements, can be determined by the methods of I, § 2.*

# VIII

# GENERAL REMARKS ABOUT FURTHER INVESTIGATIONS

## 1. Limitation of the range of the method hitherto used

For the wffs hitherto treated, the decision problem could be reduced to that for wffs with only monadic predicate variables. All these wffs, as well as the wffs of the monadic predicate calculus, are valid in a denumerably infinite domain if they are valid in any finite domain. Now there is no class of prefixes not included in the classes discussed before for which all the wffs belonging to it have this property. This has been shown by K. Schütte [1].

Let us consider the two formulas,

$$(Ex)(y)(Ez)(Gxx \vee \overline{Gxy} \vee (Gyz \mathbin{\&} \overline{Gxz})$$

and

$$(Ex)(Ey)(Ez)(u)(Gxx \vee \overline{Gxu} \vee (Gxy \mathbin{\&} Gyz \mathbin{\&} \overline{Gxz}).$$

Both these wffs are not valid in a denumerably infinite domain, e.g. in the domain $D$ of the natural numbers. Let $\Phi$ be the dyadic propositional function over $D$ which has the value $T$ for $(a, b)$ if $a<b$, and otherwise the value $F$. If $a$ and $b$ are arbitrary natural numbers, then all the formulas $\Phi(a, a)$, $\overline{\Phi(a, a+1)}$, $\Phi(a+1, b)$ & & $\overline{\Phi(a, b)}$ are false, i.e. the first formula is not valid in $D$. If $a, b, c$ are arbitrary natural numbers, then all the formulas $\Phi(a, a)$, $\overline{\Phi(a, a+1)}$, $\Phi(a, b)$ & $\Phi(b, c)$ & $\overline{\Phi(a, c)}$ are false which means that the second wff is not valid in $D$.

On the other hand, both wffs are valid in any finite domain. Let $D_1$ be such a domain, and $\Phi$ an arbitrary dyadic propositional function over $D_1$.

Let us assume that the first wff is false by the assignment $\Phi$ for $G$. There is then for every $a$ of $D_1$ an element $b$ such that for every $c$ the matrix of the wff is false by $\Phi$ and for the assignment of $a, b, c$ for $x, y, z$. For every $a$ we can select such a $b$; call it $\varphi(a)$. $\overline{\Phi(a, a)}$ and $\Phi(a, \varphi a)$ are true for every $a$. Let $\varphi_1 a, \varphi_2 a, \varphi_3 a, \ldots$

stand for $\varphi a$, $\varphi\varphi a$, $\varphi\varphi\varphi a$, .... Since $D_1$ is a finite domain, there are a certain element $c$ and a number $n$ such that $\varphi_n c = c$. Let $m$ be the smallest number such that $\Phi(a, \varphi_m a)$ is true for all $a$, while $\Phi(a, \varphi_{m+1} a)$ is not. Since $\Phi(a, \varphi_1 a)$ is always true and since $\Phi(c, \varphi_n c)$ is false, such a number $m$ exists. Let $\Phi(d, \varphi_{m+1} d)$ be false; $\Phi(\varphi d, \varphi_{m+1} d)$ & $\overline{\Phi(d, \varphi_{m+1} d)}$ is true. This means that the matrix of the wff is true by the assignment of $d$, $\varphi d$, $\varphi_{m+1} d$ for $x$, $y$, $z$, contrary to our assumption. Therefore the first wff is valid in any finite domain.

Let us suppose now that the second wff is false by the assignment of $\Phi$ for $G$ in $D_1$. Then $\Phi(a, a)$ and $\Phi(a, b)$ & $\Phi(b, c)$ & $\overline{\Phi(a, c)}$ are false for all elements $a$, $b$, $c$ of $D_1$. Furthermore, for every element $a$ of $D_1$ there is a $d$ such that $\Phi(a, d)$ is true. Let $\varphi a$ be such an element. Let $\varphi_1 a$, $\varphi_2 a$, ... have the same meaning as before. Since $D_1$ is a finite domain, there are an element $e$ and a number $n$ such that $\varphi_n e = e$. Since $\Phi(\varphi_m e, \varphi_{m+1} e)$ is true and since

$$\Phi(e, \varphi_m e) \ \& \ \Phi(\varphi_m e, \varphi_{m+1} e) \ \& \ \overline{\Phi(e, \varphi_{m+1})}$$

is false, $\Phi(e, \varphi_{m+1} e)$ would be true if $\Phi(e, \varphi_m e)$ were true. Thus $\Phi(e, \varphi_n e)$ is true, since $\Phi(e, \varphi_1 e)$ is true. This is a contradiction because $\varphi_n e = e$. Therefore, the second wff is valid in any finite domain.

The result of Schütte indicates that one may produce wffs valid in any finite domain, but not valid in a denumerably infinite domain for every prefix having at least two existential quantifiers separated by at least one universal one, and for every prefix having at least three existential quantifiers followed (immediately or not) by a universal one. The remaining prefixes are such that they contain only existential quantifiers followed by no universal quantifier, or only two existential quantifiers immediately succeeding each other, or less than two existential quantifiers. These are just the classes of prefixes for which a solution of the decision problem has been given previously and are the only classes for which a solution is known. The method of reduction to the monadic predicate calculus therefore cannot be used to solve the decision problem for further classes of prefixes, at least not in a way similar to that before.

Furthermore, the decision problem as a whole has been reduced to that for certain classes of prefixes having only three existential quantifiers, namely to that for the prefixes $(Ex)(Ey)(Ez)(u)$, or $(Ex)(Ey)(z)(Eu)$, or $(Ex)(y)(z)(Eu)(Ev)$, or $(x)(Ey)(z)(Eu)(Ev)$ (cf. J. Suranyi [1, 2]), so that it is useless trying to find the solution by any method for all wffs having prefixes which contain one of the above prefixes as a part.

For the wffs having only two existential quantifiers which do not fall under the Kalmar–Gödel–Schütte case, a solution of the problem of validity may be possible, since no statements indicating that this is impossible have been proved. The simplest prefix of this kind is $(Ex)(y)(Ez)$. For prefixes of the type $(Ex)(y)(Ez)(Eu)$ or even $(Ex)(y)(Ez_1) \ldots (Ez_m)$, a general solution has, for the present, not been excluded by a reduction theorem. But in general, the decision problem for prefixes having at least three existential quantifiers must be further specializised if progress in its solution is to be hoped for.

## 2. Some other cases for which the decision problem has been solved

Since the solution of the decision problem as a whole can be reduced to that for certain prefixes and because all prospects for its complete solution have failed, a further division into special classes of those wffs having such prefixes is necessary. For instance, the reduction of the general decision problem to that for wffs with a prefix $(Ex)(Ey)(Ez)(u)$ mentioned in § 1 has been shown shown by Suranyi, if the number of the predicate variables is not limited. Solutions might be tried therefore, if the number of the predicate variables does not exceed a given number, for instance one. No results in this direction have as yet been obtained.

Other specializations may be achieved by taking into account only special forms of the matrix. The chief results in this direction are reported below. Another division of the general division problem into special cases is given in the next chapter.

J. Herbrand [1] gave a solution for wffs with an arbitrary prefix and a matrix whose conjunctive normal form contains just one conjunction term or a matrix equivalent to such a one. As A. Church

[3] remarks, the condition for the matrix may be replaced by a weaker one if the prefix begins with $(x_1) \dots (x_m)$. It is sufficient then, that the matrix is (or is equivalent to) a disjunction in which each term is a conjunction of prime formulas or its negations, with at most one of the terms of each such conjunction containing individual variables other than $x_1, \dots, x_m$.

Th. Skolem [3, 7] has shown that the universal validity can be determined for wffs having a prefix $(Ex_1) \dots (Ex_m)(y_1) \dots (y_n)$ if the matrix is such that all prime formulas contain at least $m$ distinct variables. By the same argumentation, the universal validity can be determined for the more general case where every prime formula contains either all of the variables $x_1, \dots, x_m$ or at least one of the variables $y_1, \dots, y_m$.

For wffs having a prefix $(Ex)(y)(Ez_1) \dots (Ez_m)$, a single dyadic predicate variable, and a matrix of the form $\overline{Gxy} \vee \mathfrak{A}(z_1, \dots, z_m)$, W. Ackermann [4] gave a solution of form II of the decision problem if $m \leqslant 4$ and of form III of the decision problem for any $m$. Though the conditions which characterize these wffs are rather special, the treatment of them is of some interest because this is the only special case solved of form II of the decision problem of some generality which includes wffs that are not valid in an infinite domain, although valid in every finite domain.

I. Gégalkine [2] has solved form III of the decision problem for wffs having a prefix $(Ex)(y)(Ez_1) \dots (Ez_m)$ and a matrix $\overline{Gxy} \vee \mathfrak{A}(z_1, \dots, z_m)$, $\mathfrak{A}$ this time containing an arbitrary number of dyadic predicate variables.

The investigations concerning special cases of the decision problem, setting aside the monadic predicate calculus, nearly all concern wffs in prenex normal form. To make use of the solutions for other wffs, one has to bring them into prenex normal form. This may be done in different ways. To obtain a most favourable prenex normal form or to determine the various possible prenex normal forms, the following device may be adapted, which has been previously described in detail in connection with the wffs of the monadic predicate calculus. We consider the quantifiers whose scopes contain no other quantifiers. If they are universal quantifiers, we bring its matrix into conjunctive normal form and then contract the scope of the quantifier. It may be split into several quantifiers by using the equivalences $(x)(\mathfrak{A}(x) \,\&\, \mathfrak{B}) \leftrightarrow (x)\mathfrak{A}(x) \,\&\, \mathfrak{B}$ and $(x)(\mathfrak{A}(x) \vee \mathfrak{B}) \leftrightarrow (x)\mathfrak{A}(x) \vee \mathfrak{B}$, $(x)(\mathfrak{A}(x) \,\&\, \mathfrak{B}(x)) \leftrightarrow (x)\mathfrak{A}(x) \,\&\, (x)\mathfrak{B}(x)$. For existential quantifiers, the dual procedure is followed. After this transformation, the next innermost quantifiers are dealt with in the same manner, and so forth. The wff thus arising is put into conjunctive normal form. The validity of the wff for any domain is equivalent to the validity of all conjunction terms. Each conjunction term is then brought into prenex normal form. If there is more than one prenex normal form, we choose one with a prefix in which the maximal number of universal quantifiers is placed at the beginning. This procedure of getting a most favourable prenex normal form may also be applied to wffs which are given in prenex normal form. In the course of these transformations, there may be other simplifications. We illustrate this by the following example.

Let the wff in question be $(Ex)(y)(Ez)(Gxy \vee Gxz \,\&\, \overline{Gxy} \vee \overline{Gxz})$. It has a prefix for which no general solution of the decision problem is known. By contracting the scope of $(Ez)$, we get

$$(Ex)(y)((Gxy \,\&\, \overline{Gxy}) \vee (Gxy \,\&\, (Ez)\overline{Gxz}) \vee$$
$$\vee (\overline{Gxy} \,\&\, (Ez)Gxz) \vee (Ez)(Gxz \,\&\, \overline{Gxz})).$$

Here the disjunction terms $Gxy \,\&\, \overline{Gxy}$ and $(Ez)(Gxz \,\&\, \overline{Gxz})$ may be omitted since they get the value $F$ by any valuation. Dealing with $(y)$ in the corresponding manner, we get

$$(Ex)((y)Gxy \vee (Ez)Gxz \,\&\, (y)\overline{Gxy} \vee (Ez)\overline{Gxz} \,\&\, (Ez)Gxz \vee (Ez)\overline{Gxz}).$$

The conjunction term $(Ez)Gxz \vee (Ez)\overline{Gxz}$ may be omitted since it is universally valid. Finally, by contracting the scope of $(Ex)$, we get

$$(Ex)((y)Gxy \,\&\, (y)\overline{Gxy}) \vee (Ex)((y)Gxy \,\&\, (Ez)\overline{Gxz}) \vee$$
$$\vee (Ex)((y)\overline{Gxy} \,\&\, (Ez)Gxz) \vee (Ex)((Ez)Gxz \,\&\, (Ez)\overline{Gxz}).$$

The first three disjunction terms may be omitted as they are not valid in any domain. The wff is thus equivalent to $(Ex)((Ez)Gxz \,\&\, (Ez)\overline{Gxz})$, which has the prenex normal form $(Ex)(Ez)(Eu)(Gxz \;\&\; \overline{Gxu})$. For this prefix the decision problem is solved.

Sometimes the introduction of more predicate variables is useful. This may be illustrated by the following example. G. H. von Wright [2, 3] has given a solution of the decision problem for a class of wffs which may be described as follows. Let $\mathfrak{A}_i(x, y)$ be a wff with the free individual variables $x$, $y$ and without quantifiers. The predicate variables occurring in it are dyadic ones. Let $\mathfrak{B}_k(x)$ be a wff, the $P$-constituents of which are of the form $(Ey)\mathfrak{A}_i(x, y)$. Further, let $\mathfrak{C}$ be a wff, the $P$-constituents of which have the form $(Ex)\mathfrak{B}_k(x)$. Von Wright has determined the validity of these wffs $\mathfrak{C}$ by independent methods. But by introducing more predicate variables, we can transform the wffs $\mathfrak{C}$ into a conjunction of wffs having the prefix of VII, § 2. Let $(Ey)\mathfrak{A}_1(x, y), \ldots, (Ey)\mathfrak{A}_l(x, y)$ be the different formulas $(Ey)\mathfrak{A}_i(x, y)$ occurring in $\mathfrak{C}$. To each $(Ey)\mathfrak{A}_i(x, y)$ we let correspond a monadic predicate variable $G_i$ not occurring in $\mathfrak{C}$. Let $\mathfrak{C}$ become $\mathfrak{C}'$ if every $(Ey)\mathfrak{A}_i(x, y)$ is replaced by $G_i x$. The validity of $\mathfrak{C}$ for an arbitrary domain is equivalent to the validity of the following wff $\mathfrak{D}$:

$$(Ex)(Ey)(z)((G_1x \;\&\; \overline{\mathfrak{A}_1(x,z)}) \vee (\overline{G_1x} \;\&\; \mathfrak{A}_1(x,y)) \vee \ldots \vee$$
$$\vee\, (Ex)(Ey)(z)((G_lx \;\&\; \overline{\mathfrak{A}_l(x,z)}) \vee (\overline{G_lx} \;\&\; \mathfrak{A}_l(x,y))) \vee \mathfrak{C}';$$

for

$$(Ex)(Ey)(z)((G_ix \;\&\; \overline{\mathfrak{A}_i(x,z)}) \vee (\overline{G_ix} \;\&\; \mathfrak{A}_i(x, y)))$$

is a prenex normal form of the wff

$$\overline{(x)(G_ix \leftrightarrow (Ey)\mathfrak{A}_i(x, y))}.$$

If we bring $\mathfrak{C}$ into conjunctive normal form, each conjunction term has a form

$$(Ex)\mathfrak{B}_{k_1}(x) \vee \ldots \vee (Ex)\mathfrak{B}_{k_m}(x) \vee (x)\overline{\mathfrak{B}}_{i_1}(x) \vee \ldots \vee (x)\overline{\mathfrak{B}}_{i_n}(x).$$

Instead of the last formula, we may write

$$(Ex)(\mathfrak{B}_{k_1}(x) \vee \ldots \vee \mathfrak{B}_{k_m}(x)) \vee (x)\overline{\mathfrak{B}}_{i_1}(x) \vee \ldots \vee (x)\overline{\mathfrak{B}}_{i_n}(x) \text{ or}$$
$$(Ex)(z_1) \ldots (z_n)(\mathfrak{B}_{k_1}(x) \vee \ldots \vee \mathfrak{B}_{k_m}(x) \vee \overline{\mathfrak{B}}_{i_1}(z_1) \vee \ldots \vee \overline{\mathfrak{B}}_{i_n}(z_n)).$$

Therefore, $\mathfrak{C}'$ can be brought into a conjunctive normal form $\mathfrak{C}_1' \,\&\, \dots \,\&\, \mathfrak{C}_j'$ in which every conjunction term is in prenex normal form and has a prefix $(Ex)(z_1) \dots (z_n)$.

The validity of $\mathfrak{D}$ means the validity of all wffs $\mathfrak{D}_i$ which arise from $\mathfrak{D}$ by replacing $\mathfrak{C}'$ by some $\mathfrak{C}_i'$. Every $\mathfrak{D}_i$ can be given a prenex normal form with a prefix $(Ex)(Ey)(z_1) \dots (z_p)$, since the existential quantifiers can be placed first and because their number can be reduced to two by making use of the equivalence between $(Ex)\mathfrak{A}(x) \vee (Ex)\mathfrak{B}(x)$ and $(Ex)(\mathfrak{A}(x) \vee \mathfrak{B}(x))$. The validity of a wff $\mathfrak{C}$ is thus reduced to the validity of a finite number of wffs having the Kalmar–Gödel–Schütte prefix.

The method of producing an advantageous prenex normal form in the way described first (without introducing new predicate variables) leads to a solution of the decision problem only for wffs with a special structure. A. Church [3], among others, mentions the following simple cases in which a solution of the decision problem can be achieved in this way.

1) The $P$-constituents of the wff in question can be brought into prenex normal form such that their prefixes consist solely of universal quantifiers or solely of existential quantifiers.

2) The $P$-constituents can be brought into prenex normal form such that their prefixes are all of the form $(x_1)(x_2)(Ey_1)(Ey_2)$ or of a form resulting from this by deleting one or more quantifiers.

3) Each $P$-constituent can be brought into prenex normal form such that its prefix has one of the forms $(x_1) \dots (x_m)(Ey_1) \dots (Ey_n)$ or $(Ex_1) \dots (Ex_m)(y_1) \dots (y_n)$, where $n$ is the same number for each prefix and $0 \leqslant m \leqslant n$, and such that every prime formula contains all of the variables $y_1, \dots, y_n$.

4) The wff begins with $(x_1) \dots (x_m)$, the scopes of the quantifiers extending to the end of the formula. Every prime formula has at most one individual variable different from $x_1, \dots, x_m$.

Indeed, in the first case a prenex normal form with the prefix of VI, § 5 can be obtained; in the second case a similar one with the prefix of VII, § 2. The third case can be reduced to the case treated by Skolem and mentioned previously. In the fourth case, the wff can be treated in the same way as wffs having only monadic predicate variables.

Further cases could be added, e.g. the case that each $P$-constituent has a prefix $(x_1) \dots (x_m)(Ey_1)(Ey_2)(z_1) \dots (z_n)$ or a prefix which is a part of this prefix, no $P$-constituent standing under a negation-bar. A general characterization of the wffs for which the decidability can be shown in this way seems difficult. But since the procedure by which an advantageous prenex normal form can be obtained is easy to achieve with a given wff, it seems more important to ask what can be done with a wff for which all attempts to obtain one of the favourable prefixes fail. This will be discussed in § 3.

## 3. A general theorem about the validity of wffs

The following statements concern wffs which may also have free individual variables. Wffs containing equality are not considered here.

Let a wff $\mathfrak{A}$ be given in prenex normal form. We consider the following alterations which could be effected on $\mathfrak{A}$.

a) A universal quantifier with which the prefix begins is dropped.

b) An existential quantifier with which the prefix begins is dropped, provided that the wff contains no free individual variables.

c) An existential quantifier somewhere in the prefix is dropped. The variable of the matrix belonging to this quantifier is replaced everywhere by the same free individual variable occurring in $\mathfrak{A}$, or this variable is replaced everywhere by the variable of a quantifier preceding the existential one.

d) The matrix of $\mathfrak{A}$ is put into the form of a disjunction and one or more of the disjunction terms are left out, vacuous quantifiers, i.e. such quantifiers for which there are no more variables in the matrix, being deleted.

By any of these transformations, or by a series of such transformations, $\mathfrak{A}$ becomes a wff $\mathfrak{A}'$ which is valid only for domains in which $\mathfrak{A}$ is also valid. If $\mathfrak{A}'$ has or can be given a prefix for which the decision problem is solved, we may thereby find domains in which $\mathfrak{A}$ is valid. Especially, $\mathfrak{A}$ is universally valid if $\mathfrak{A}'$ is.

We give some examples.

(1) The wff $(Ex)(y)(Ez)(Gxx \vee \overline{Gyy} \vee (Gxz \vee Gyz \ \& \ Gzx \vee Gzy))$ is universally valid. For by d), we get $(Ex)(y)(Gxx \vee \overline{Gyy})$ which has the other prenex normal form $(y)(Ex)(Gxx \vee \overline{Gyy})$ and which proves universally valid by the criterion given for wffs with this prefix. To the last formula we may also apply the transformation c) and get $(y)(Gyy \vee \overline{Gyy})$ which is recognized as universally valid since it has a tautologous matrix.

$$(2) \quad \begin{cases} (Ex)(y)(Ez)(Eu)(Gxx \vee \overline{Gxy} \vee (Gxz \ \& \ Gzx) \vee \\ \vee (Gxz \ \& \ Gzu \ \& \ \overline{Gxz}) \vee (Gxz \ \& \ Gxu \ \& \ \overline{Gzu}) \end{cases}$$

is universall valid. By applying the transformation c) and replacing $z$ and $u$ by $y$, we get

$$(Ex)(y)(Gxx \vee \overline{Gxy} \vee (Gxy \ \& \ Gyx) \vee (Gxy \ \& \ Gyy \ \& \ \overline{Gxy}) \vee \\ \vee (Gxy \ \& \ Gxy \ \& \ \overline{Gyy})$$

which may be recognized as universally valid by the methods given for the prefix $(Ex)(y)$, or which may be further simplified by the transformation d) to $(Ex)(y)(Gxx \vee \overline{Gxy} \vee (Gxy \ \& \ Gxy \ \& \ \overline{Gyy})$. By an equivalence transformation of the matrix, we get

$$(Ex)(y)(Gxx \vee \overline{Gxy} \vee \overline{Gyy}).$$

By a further application of d), we get $(Ex)(y)(Gxx \vee \overline{Gyy})$ which has been dealt with above.

Sometimes we may not be able to decide the validity of a wff $\mathfrak{A}$ in this way, but success may be gained if we take a finite disjunction $\mathfrak{A} \vee \mathfrak{A} \vee \ldots \vee \mathfrak{A}$ instead of $\mathfrak{A}$ and bring it somehow into prenex normal form.

(3) To give an example for this case also, we consider the wff

$$(Ex)(y)(Ez)(Gxx \vee Gxy \vee \overline{Gyx} \vee Gyy \vee Gxz \vee Gzz \vee (Gzx \ \& \ Gyz))$$

which we abbreviate $(Ex)(y)(Ez)\mathfrak{A}(x, y, z)$. Here the universal validity cannot be shown as in example (2). But if we take $(Ex)(y)(Ez)\mathfrak{A}(x, y, z) \vee (Ex)(y)(Ez)\mathfrak{A}(x, y, z)$, for which

$$(Ex)(y)(Ez)(Eu)(v)(Ew)(\mathfrak{A}(x, y, z) \vee \mathfrak{A}(u, v, w))$$

is a prenex normal form, and transform it by c) into

$$(Ex)(y)(Ez)(v)(\mathfrak{A}(x, y, z) \vee \mathfrak{A}(y, v, x)),$$

the matrix becomes a tautology.

*The question may be raised whether any universally valid wff can be recognized as such in the last manner by starting from a finite disjunction of the wff. The answer is positive.*

A theorem of this kind shall be proved, but only for wffs in which the negation-bar stands at most over prime formulas and in which no quantifiers are part of a conjunction term. This is sufficient for all applications since every wff can be given such a form. For instance, a prenex normal form fulfills the condition.

To formulate our statement more precisely, we introduce the notion of *n-validity.*

We first construct for every wff $\mathfrak{A}$ a finite set of other wffs determined by $\mathfrak{A}$. A wff of this set may be designated by $\langle\mathfrak{A}\rangle$ though there are usually several wffs $\langle\mathfrak{A}\rangle$. We define the wffs $\langle\mathfrak{A}\rangle$ by recurrence from a wff to its parts according to the following conditions.

(1) If $\mathfrak{A}$ has no quantifiers, $\langle\mathfrak{A}\rangle$ is $\mathfrak{A}$.

(2) $\langle(x)\mathfrak{A}(x)\rangle$ is either $(x)\mathfrak{A}(x) \vee (x)\mathfrak{A}(x)$ or $(x)\langle\mathfrak{A}(x)\rangle$.

(3) $\langle(Ex)\mathfrak{A}(x)\rangle$ is either $(Ex)\mathfrak{A}(x) \vee (Ex)\mathfrak{A}(x)$ or $(Ex)\langle\mathfrak{A}(x)\rangle$.

(4) $\langle\mathfrak{A} \vee \mathfrak{B}\rangle$ is $\langle\mathfrak{A}\rangle \vee \langle\mathfrak{B}\rangle$.

If we have for instance a wff $(x)(Ey)\mathfrak{A}(x, y)$ in which $\mathfrak{A}(x, y)$ contains no quantifiers, the wffs $\langle(x)(Ey)\mathfrak{A}(x, y)\rangle$ are the wffs $(x)(Ey)\mathfrak{A}(x, y) \vee (x)(Ey)\mathfrak{A}(x, y)$, $(x)((Ey)\mathfrak{A}(x, y) \vee (Ey)\mathfrak{A}(x, y))$, and $(x)(Ey)\mathfrak{A}(x, y)$.

*A wff $\mathfrak{A}$ is called* 1-*valid if there is a prenex normal form of $\mathfrak{A}$ which may be turned into a tautology without quantifiers by transformations* (*a*)–(*c*). ((d) is not used here.)

The prenex normal forms of $\mathfrak{A}$ which are used here constitute a definite finite set. After $\mathfrak{A}$ has been transformed in a way such that the negation-bar stands only over prime formulas, and after the variables have been, if necessary, rewritten so that different quantifiers have different variables, the prenex normal forms result by placing the quantifiers at the beginning in a succession such that any quantifier which was in the scope of another quantifier remains so afterwards.

$\mathfrak{A}$ *is called* $n+1$*-valid if one of the wffs* $\langle\mathfrak{A}\rangle$ *is* $n$*-valid.*

We now state the following theorem: T VIII *For every universally valid wff* (having the special form as regards the position of the negation-bar and as regards the conjunction terms) *there is an* $n$ *such that the wff is* $n$*-valid.*

This of course does not include a solution of the decision problem in form I, since in general we cannot determine the number $n$. The theorem we deliver here is related, as may be mentioned, to another one of that kind expressed in a more number-theoretic form. The latter theorem is a corollary of the Gödel method of proof for the completeness of the first order predicate calculus (K. Gödel [1]) (cf. the generalized metatheorem of A. Church [3]). A proof of our theorem has been given by J. Herbrand [1] in proving what he calls the property A of universally valid wffs. On the other hand, properties *B* and *C* of universally valid wffs also mentioned in his paper and shown to be equivalent to *A*, are in close relation to the metatheorem above.

We shall not give the proof of Herbrand or any other self-contained proof here, but we make use of the result of Gödel that a certain axiomatic system delivers all universally valid wffs. But no reference is made to the Gödel method of proof. Our theorem may be easily established by means of an axiomatic system in which all universally valid wffs can be derived and for which the Hauptsatz of G. Gentzen [1] or an equivalent for it is valid.

We take an axiomatic system given by K. Schütte [3] which is most appropiate for our purpose. This system has been shown by Schütte to be equivalent to the system which Gödel has proved to be complete, and to contain an equivalent of the Hauptsatz. We shall show that the axioms of this system are $n$-valid and that each rule of inference includes a transition from $n$-valid wffs to $m$-valid wffs.

The postulates of the system are the following:

(1) Axioms are all wffs $\mathfrak{A} \vee \overline{\mathfrak{A}}$ where $\mathfrak{A}$ is a prime formula.

(2) The rules of inference contain a transition from

(2a) $\mathfrak{M} \vee \mathfrak{A} \vee \mathfrak{B} \vee \mathfrak{N}$ to $\mathfrak{M} \vee \mathfrak{B} \vee \mathfrak{A} \vee \mathfrak{N}$,

(2b) $\mathfrak{A} \vee \mathfrak{A} \vee \mathfrak{N}$ to $\mathfrak{A} \vee \mathfrak{N}$,

(2c) $\mathfrak{A}$ to $\mathfrak{A} \vee \mathfrak{B}$,

(2d) $\overline{\mathfrak{A}} \vee \mathfrak{N}$ and $\overline{\mathfrak{B}} \vee \mathfrak{N}$ to $\overline{\mathfrak{A} \vee \mathfrak{B}} \vee \mathfrak{N}$,

(2e) $\mathfrak{A} \vee \mathfrak{N}$ to $\overline{\overline{\mathfrak{A}}} \vee \mathfrak{N}$,

(2f) $\mathfrak{A}(\mathfrak{v}) \vee \mathfrak{N}$ to $(E\mathfrak{u})\mathfrak{A}(\mathfrak{u}) \vee \mathfrak{N}$, and

(2g) $\overline{\mathfrak{A}(\mathfrak{v})} \vee \mathfrak{N}$ to $\overline{(E\mathfrak{v})\mathfrak{A}(\mathfrak{v})} \vee \mathfrak{N}$.

The system is formulated with free variables. In (2g), $\mathfrak{N}$ must not contain the variable $\mathfrak{v}$. The rules (2a)–(2g) are to be so understood that the disjunction terms $\mathfrak{M}$ and $\mathfrak{N}$ may also be missing. Conjunction and the universal quantifier do not appear in the system. $\mathfrak{A}$ & $\mathfrak{B}$ is interpreted as being an abbreviation for $\overline{\overline{\mathfrak{A}} \vee \overline{\mathfrak{B}}}$; $(x)\mathfrak{A}(x)$ is such a one for $\overline{(Ex)\overline{\mathfrak{A}(x)}}$.

Let us consider now a wff $\mathfrak{A}$ which is universally valid, in which the negation-bar stands only over prime formulas, and in which no conjunction term contains quantifiers. If $\mathfrak{A}$ contains a universal quantifier or the sign of conjunction, we eliminate them in the above-mentioned way. $\mathfrak{A}$ then becomes a wff $\mathfrak{A}'$. Because the system of axioms is complete, a proof can be given of $\mathfrak{A}'$.

We now transform every wff $\mathfrak{B}$ of the proof into another wff $|\mathfrak{B}|$ in which the negation-bar stands only over prime formulas. This can be done in a unique way as described previously in chapter II. We proceed from the whole wff to its parts by using the fact that $|\mathfrak{A} \vee \mathfrak{B}|$ is $|\mathfrak{A}| \vee |\mathfrak{B}|$, $|(Ex)\mathfrak{A}(x)|$ is $(Ex)|\mathfrak{A}(x)|$, $|\overline{\overline{\mathfrak{A}}}|$ is $|\mathfrak{A}|$, $|\overline{\mathfrak{A} \vee \mathfrak{B}}|$ is $|\overline{\mathfrak{A}}|$ & $|\overline{\mathfrak{B}}|$, $|\overline{(E\mathfrak{u})\mathfrak{A}(\mathfrak{u})}|$ is $(\mathfrak{u})|\overline{\mathfrak{A}(\mathfrak{u})}|$, $|\mathfrak{A}$ & $\mathfrak{B}|$ is $|\mathfrak{A}|$ & $|\mathfrak{B}|$, $|\overline{\mathfrak{A} \,\&\, \mathfrak{B}}|$ is $|\overline{\mathfrak{A}}| \vee |\overline{\mathfrak{B}}|$, $|\overline{(\mathfrak{u})\mathfrak{A}(\mathfrak{u})}|$ is $(E\mathfrak{u})|\overline{\mathfrak{A}(\mathfrak{u})}|$, till the wff has the desired form. By this transformation, universal quantifiers and the conjunction sign may again appear in the wffs. Obviously, $\mathfrak{A}'$ is again transformed into $\mathfrak{A}$.

The axioms (1) are unaffected by this transformation. Though, as regards the rules (2a), (2b), (2c), (2f) both premise and conclusion may be altered, the connection of the wffs by these rules remains. In (2e), premise and conclusion are transformed into the same wff. The wffs formerly connected by (2d) are now related by a transition (2d′) from $\mathfrak{C} \vee \mathfrak{E}$ and $\mathfrak{D} \vee \mathfrak{E}$ to $(\mathfrak{C} \,\&\, \mathfrak{D}) \vee \mathfrak{E}$. Instead of (2g) we have now a transition (2g′) from $\mathfrak{B}(\mathfrak{v}) \vee \mathfrak{N}$ to $(\mathfrak{v})\mathfrak{B}(\mathfrak{v}) \vee \mathfrak{N}$. No wff of the transformed proof contains as a part a conjunction with quantifiers in its terms; for the last wff of the proof has no such conjunctions, and the premises of (2a), (2b), (2c), (2d′), (2f), and (2g′) cannot contain it if the conclusion does not.

We show that every wff of the transformed proof is $n$-valid for some $n$. For the axioms (1) this is evident. They are 1-valid. If $\mathfrak{M} \vee \mathfrak{A} \vee \mathfrak{B} \vee \mathfrak{N}$ is $n$-valid, then $\mathfrak{M} \vee \mathfrak{B} \vee \mathfrak{A} \vee \mathfrak{N}$ is $n$-valid for the same $n$; for if $n=1$, $\mathfrak{M} \vee \mathfrak{B} \vee \mathfrak{A} \vee \mathfrak{N}$ can be given a prenex normal form with the same prefix as $\mathfrak{M} \vee \mathfrak{A} \vee \mathfrak{B} \vee \mathfrak{N}$. All other steps can be done correspondingly, the prefixes of the corresponding wffs being the same and the matrices differing only by the arrangement of the disjunction terms. If $\mathfrak{M} \vee \mathfrak{A} \vee \mathfrak{B} \vee \mathfrak{N}$ is $n+1$-valid, we have a certain wff $\langle \mathfrak{M} \vee \mathfrak{A} \vee \mathfrak{B} \vee \mathfrak{N} \rangle$ which is $n$-valid. We then find a wff $\langle \mathfrak{M} \vee \mathfrak{B} \vee \mathfrak{A} \vee \mathfrak{N} \rangle$ differing from the former one by the succession of the disjunction terms. Thus the statement proves correct by induction on $n$.

If $\mathfrak{A}$ is $n$-valid, $\mathfrak{A} \vee \mathfrak{B}$ is $n$-valid; for if $n=1$, $\mathfrak{A} \vee \mathfrak{B}$ can be given a prefix of which the prefix given to $\mathfrak{A}$ is the first part, the matrix of $\mathfrak{A} \vee \mathfrak{B}$ containing one disjunction term more than that of $\mathfrak{A}$. This relation between the two corresponding wffs can be preserved by all succeeding steps. If $\mathfrak{A}$ has been transformed into a tautology without quantifiers, $\mathfrak{A} \vee \mathfrak{B}$ is transformed into such a tautology by further steps which drop the rest of the quantifiers according to (a)–(c). If $n > 1$ and if we have a wff $\langle \mathfrak{A} \rangle$, a wff $\langle \mathfrak{A} \vee \mathfrak{B} \rangle$ exists of which $\langle \mathfrak{A} \rangle$ is a disjunction term. The statement for $n+1$ is thus reduced to that for $n$.

If $\mathfrak{A} \vee \mathfrak{A} \vee \mathfrak{N}$ is $n$-valid, $\mathfrak{A} \vee \mathfrak{N}$ is $n+1$-valid; for $\mathfrak{A} \vee \mathfrak{A} \vee \mathfrak{N}$ is one of the wffs $\langle \mathfrak{A} \vee \mathfrak{N} \rangle$ (or results from it by changing the succession of disjunction terms and doubling such terms without quantifiers).

If $\mathfrak{A} \vee \mathfrak{C}$ is $m$-valid and $\mathfrak{B} \vee \mathfrak{C}$ is $n$-valid, $(\mathfrak{A} \,\&\, \mathfrak{B}) \vee \mathfrak{C}$ is Max $(m, n)+1$-valid. (Remember that $\mathfrak{A}$ and $\mathfrak{B}$ contain no quantifiers.) If both $m$ and $n$ are 1, $(\mathfrak{A} \,\&\, \mathfrak{B}) \vee \mathfrak{C} \vee \mathfrak{C}$ is 1-valid; for we can give this wff a prenex normal form such that the prefix of $\mathfrak{A} \vee \mathfrak{C}$ comes first, followed by the prefix of $\mathfrak{B} \vee \mathfrak{C}$. The first part of the prefix can be transformed by (a)–(c) in the same way as the prefix of $\mathfrak{A} \vee \mathfrak{C}$. After these quantifiers have disappeared, we treat the second part of the prefix and the part of the matrix belonging to it in the same way as $\mathfrak{B} \vee \mathfrak{C}$. Obviously, $(\mathfrak{A} \ \& \ \mathfrak{B}) \vee \mathfrak{C} \vee \mathfrak{C}$ is then transformed into a tautology without quantifiers. $(\mathfrak{A} \ \& \ \mathfrak{B}) \vee \mathfrak{C} \vee \mathfrak{C}$ is one of the wffs $\langle(\mathfrak{A} \ \& \ \mathfrak{B}) \vee \mathfrak{C}\rangle$ or differs from such a wff by another succession of disjunction terms and by writing twice some disjunction terms without quantifiers, which evidently has no effect on the property of $n$-validity. Therefore $(\mathfrak{A} \ \& \ \mathfrak{B}) \vee \mathfrak{C}$ is 2-valid. Let us in the general case designate by $\langle\mathfrak{A}_n\rangle$ a wff generated from $\mathfrak{A}$ by $n$-fold application of $\langle \ \ \rangle$ $(n \geqq 0)$. If $\mathfrak{A} \vee \mathfrak{C}$ is $m$-valid and if $\mathfrak{B} \vee \mathfrak{C}$ is $n$-valid, a certain wff $\mathfrak{A} \vee \langle\mathfrak{C}\rangle_{m-1}$ and a certain wff $\mathfrak{B} \vee \langle\mathfrak{C}\rangle_{n-1}$ are 1-valid. Then a wff $(\mathfrak{A} \& \mathfrak{B}) \vee \langle\mathfrak{C}\rangle_{m-1} \vee \langle\mathfrak{C}\rangle_{n-1}$ is 1-valid, which shows in the same way as the 1-validity of $(\mathfrak{A} \ \& \ \mathfrak{B}) \vee \mathfrak{C} \vee \mathfrak{C}$ before. Consequently, a wff $(\mathfrak{A} \ \& \ \mathfrak{B}) \vee \langle\mathfrak{C} \vee \mathfrak{C}\rangle_{\mathrm{Max}\,(m,n)-1}$ is 1-valid. This means that $(\mathfrak{A} \ \& \ \mathfrak{B}) \vee \mathfrak{C} \vee \mathfrak{C}$ is Max$(m,n)$-valid. Then $(\mathfrak{A} \ \& \ \mathfrak{B}) \vee \mathfrak{C}$ is Max$(m,n)+1$-valid. Our statement is therefore proved.

If $\mathfrak{A}(\mathfrak{v}) \vee \mathfrak{R}$ is $n$-valid, $(E\mathfrak{u})\mathfrak{A}(\mathfrak{u}) \vee \mathfrak{R}$ is $n$-valid. If $n=1$, we can give $(E\mathfrak{u})\mathfrak{A}(\mathfrak{u}) \vee \mathfrak{R}$ a prenex normal form such that it can be transformed by (b) or (c) into a prenex normal form of $\mathfrak{A}(\mathfrak{v}) \vee \mathfrak{R}$, the latter being chosen arbitrarily. If $\mathfrak{A}(\mathfrak{v}) \vee \mathfrak{R}$ is $n+1$-valid, some wff $\langle\mathfrak{A}(\mathfrak{v})\rangle \vee \langle\mathfrak{R}\rangle$ is $n$-valid. Supposing the statement to be true for $n$, we conclude that $(E\mathfrak{v})\langle\mathfrak{A}(\mathfrak{v})\rangle \vee \langle\mathfrak{R}\rangle$ is $n$-valid. Since $(E\mathfrak{v})\langle\mathfrak{A}(\mathfrak{v})\rangle \vee \langle\mathfrak{R}\rangle$ is one of the wffs $\langle(E\mathfrak{v})\mathfrak{A}(\mathfrak{v}) \vee \mathfrak{R}\rangle$, $(E\mathfrak{v})\mathfrak{A}(\mathfrak{v}) \vee \mathfrak{R}$ is $n+1$-valid.

If $\mathfrak{A}(\mathfrak{v}) \vee \mathfrak{R}$ is $n$-valid, $(\mathfrak{v})\mathfrak{A}(\mathfrak{v}) \vee \mathfrak{R}$ is $n$-valid. If $n=1$ and some prenex normal form of $\mathfrak{A}(\mathfrak{v}) \vee \mathfrak{R}$ is given, there is a prenex normal form of $(\mathfrak{v})\mathfrak{A}(\mathfrak{v}) \vee \mathfrak{R}$ which is the same as the former one except that the universal quantifier $(\mathfrak{v})$ is placed at the beginning of the prefix. By transformation (a), this quantifier can be dropped. If $\mathfrak{A}(\mathfrak{v}) \vee \mathfrak{R}$ is $n+1$-valid, $(\mathfrak{v})\mathfrak{A}(\mathfrak{v}) \vee \mathfrak{R}$ is $n+1$-valid. This is demonstrated in the same way as the corresponding statement for $(E\mathfrak{v})\mathfrak{A}(\mathfrak{v}) \vee \mathfrak{R}$.

This completes the proof of our theorem.

*The proven theorem may be helpful if the universal validity for a class of wffs has to be decided. For by separating the wffs which are*

*$n$-valid where $n$ is less than a fixed number, the subset of the wffs for which the universal validity is doubtful is diminished.* Sometimes we may even succeed in determining all wffs $n$-valid for some $n$.

*To reduce further the number of these wffs, other rules might be useful by which certain wffs are shown not to be universally valid.*

The following transformations ($\alpha$)–($\gamma$) concerning wffs in prenex normal form are in a certain sense the inverses of the former transformations (b), (c), (d). While transformations (a)–(d) defined a transition from a statement to a stronger statement, ($\alpha$)–($\gamma$) contain a transition to a weaker statement.

($\alpha$) A universal quantifier appearing anywhere in the prefix is changed into an existential one.

($\beta$) A universal quantifier appearing anywhere in the prefix is dropped. The variable pertaining to it is everywhere replaced by a free individual variable occurring in the wff, or is replaced by a variable belonging to a quantifier preceding the universal one.

($\gamma$) The matrix of the wff is brought into the form of a conjunction, and one or more of the conjunction terms are omitted.

If by ($\alpha$)–($\gamma$) we can transform a wff into another one recognized not to be universally valid, the given wff is not universally valid. Sometimes this method may fail, but we may succeed when starting from a finite conjunction $\mathfrak{A}$ & $\mathfrak{A}$ & ... & $\mathfrak{A}$ instead of from $\mathfrak{A}$. Another device of finding wffs not universally valid is to determine the wffs which are not valid in a domain with a fixed finite number of elements. Finally, we may construct special propositional functions in the domain of the natural numbers, which assigned to the predicate variables of the wff yield necessary conditions for validity in that domain. Wffs not satisfying these conditions are not universally valid.

# IX

# THE DECISION PROBLEM FOR WFFS WITH FUNCTIONAL VARIABLES

## 1. Introduction of wffs with functional variables

In this chapter we give another formulation of the decision problem which may be employed to obtain a classification of special cases different from that mentioned previously. It has been customary to base the logical calculus upon the primitive idea of the predicate or the propositional function. But it would be just as convenient to use the notion of function in the mathematical sense, i.e. of a function whose domain and range are the elements of a certain domain. Such functions will be referred to simply as functions in the following. Though special logical systems have been constructed with the fundamental idea of function, it seems that the decision problem in general for such a functional calculus, apart from special systems with a mathematical interpretation, never has been taken into consideration.

For all applications of logic, a functional calculus would render the same service as a predicate calculus. Corresponding to every monadic propositional function $\Phi$ over some domain, for instance, we can find a function $\varphi$ over that domain such that for every element of this domain "$\Phi(a)$ is true" and "$\varphi(a)=a$" are equivalent statements. Likewise, "$\varphi(a, b)=a$" and "$\Phi(a, b)$ is true" can be equivalent statements. There are of course many other ways of finding an equivalent expression for "$\Phi(a)$ is true" by means of a function. For instance, if $b_0$ and $c_0$ are two fixed elements of the domain, then there is a function $\varphi$ such that $\varphi(a)$ is always $b_0$ or $c_0$, and such that $\varphi a=b_0$ and $\varphi a=c_0$ correspond to "$\Phi(a)$ is true" and to "$\Phi(a)$ is false". But the first way seems preferable with respect to the formalization, since we need not introduce special elements of the domain in question and special properties of the functions. For the rest, the method which we choose is not essential for the following. The equivalence between the wffs with predicate variables and the wffs with functional variables will be stated more exactly in that which follows. We now proceed to give the notion of a wff for the functional calculus. Since several notions of the first chapter are repeated or undergo only a slight alteration, we shall be rather brief in the succeeding explanations.

The *primitive symbols* are the *logical constants* "&", "v", "—", "="; the *individual variables* $x, y, z, x_1, \ldots$; the *functional variables* $f^1, g^1, h^1, f^2, h^3, \ldots$, the superscript $n$ indicating the $n$-adic character of the functional variable. There are further existential and universal quantifiers for the individual and the functional variables for which the same (the corresponding) notation is used as before.

A *term* (or more precisely an individual term) is an individual variable or an $n$-adic functional variable succeeded by $n$ individual variables. $\mathfrak{a}, \mathfrak{b}, \mathfrak{c}, \ldots$, which were syntactical variables for individual variables before, are now *syntactical variables for terms*. Syntactical variables for wffs are the same as before.

A *well-formed formula* is a combination of symbols which can be generated by a finite application of the following rules.

*W'*1. A wff is obtained by placing a term before, and another after the sign "=". These are the *prime formulas*.

*W'*2. The construction of further wffs by use of the signs "&", "v", "–", and the quantifiers is carried out in the same way, or the corresponding way, as by rules *W*4–*W*6 of chapter I.

The same applies to the definition of free and bound individual and functional variables. Among the wffs defined in this manner, are included the equality formulas (chapter III). The superscript of a functional variable is usually omitted.

We get an *n-adic function* in a domain $D$ if we let correspond to each $n$-tuple of elements of $D$ one element of $D$, uniquely determined. In a finite domain, there is only a finite number of *n-adic functions* for every $n$. Functions are designated by Greek minuscules such as $\varphi, \chi, \psi, \varphi_1, \ldots$. Elements of a domain are designated by $a, b, c, d, \ldots$, or by the same letters with number indices. A *complete assignment* for a wff with free individual or functional variables is established in a domain $D$ if an element of $D$ is assigned to every free individual variable, and a function over $D$ with the same $n$-adic character to every free functional variable occurring in the wff. A complete assignment for a wff without free variables is a vacuous one.

By a complete assignment for a wff, an element of the domain corresponds to every term containing only free variables, of the wff. This is called the *value* of the term. The value of an individual variable is the element assigned to it. The value of a term $f^n x_1 \dots x_n$ is the value of the function assigned to $f^n$ for the $n$-tuple $(a_1, \dots, a_n)$, where each $a_i$ is the element assigned to $x_i$. Correspondingly for other variables.

By any complete assignment for a wff, a value ($T$ or $F$) is determined by recursion according to the following rules.

$V'1$. A wff $\mathfrak{a} = \mathfrak{b}$ has the value $T$ or $F$, according as the values of $\mathfrak{a}$ and $\mathfrak{b}$ are the same or not.

$V'2 - V'4$. These valuation rules exactly correspond to rules $V4 - V6$ of chapter I.

Definitions of *validity* and *satisfiability* are the analogues of those of chapters I and II.

For domains with a fixed finite number of individuals, the valuation of a given wff can be effectively carried out, since not only the number of individuals, but also the number of $n$-adic functions is finite for every $n$.

The *decision problem* for the functional calculus is defined, as in chapter II, in the three forms I—III.

## 2. Special cases for which the decision problem is solved for wffs with functional variables

We shall restrict ourselves here to the problem of validity for wffs in prenex normal form having functional variables with no quantifiers. This corresponds to the decision problem for the wffs of the first order predicate calculus.

Special cases of the decision problem are obtained by considering special prefixes or classes of prefixes and by eventually limiting the number of the functional variables occurring in the wffs. Such a special class of wffs would correspond to classes of wffs of the predicate calculus with special matrices. On the other hand, to every class of wffs of the predicate calculus with certain prefixes there correspond here wffs with the same prefixes, but with special matrices. This correspondence of course depends upon how we establish the correspondence between propositional functions and functions. We adhere to the method previously mentioned.

Let a wff $\mathfrak{A}(G_1, \ldots, G_k)$ of the predicate calculus without bound predicate variables be given. Let $\mathfrak{f}_1, \ldots, \mathfrak{f}_k$ be functional variables, each $\mathfrak{f}_i$ being an $n$-adic variable if $G_i$ is an $n$-adic variable. In $\mathfrak{A}(G_1, \ldots, G_k)$, we replace every prime formula $G_i\mathfrak{a}_1 \ldots \mathfrak{a}_m$ by $\mathfrak{f}_i\mathfrak{a}_1 \ldots \mathfrak{a}_m = \mathfrak{a}_1$, by which $\mathfrak{A}(G_1, \ldots, G_k)$ becomes $\mathfrak{B}(\mathfrak{f}_1, \ldots, \mathfrak{f}_k)$. The validity of $\mathfrak{A}(G_1, \ldots, G_k)$ holds for some domain, if the validity of $\mathfrak{B}(\mathfrak{f}_1, \ldots, \mathfrak{f}_k)$ holds for this domain, and vice versa.

On the other hand, let $\mathfrak{C}(\mathfrak{f}_1, \ldots, \mathfrak{f}_k)$ be a wff according to $W'1-W'2$ without bound functional variables. Further, let $G_1, \ldots, G_k$ be predicate variables, each $G_i$ being an $m+1$-adic predicate variable, if $\mathfrak{f}_i$ is an $m$-adic functional variable. Let $\mathfrak{D}(G_1, \ldots, G_k)$ result from $\mathfrak{C}(\mathfrak{f}_1, \ldots, \mathfrak{f}_k)$ by replacing any prime formula $\mathfrak{f}_i\mathfrak{a}_1 \ldots \mathfrak{a}_m = \mathfrak{b}$ or $\mathfrak{b} = \mathfrak{f}_i\mathfrak{a}_1 \ldots \mathfrak{a}_m$ by $G_i\mathfrak{a}_1 \ldots \mathfrak{a}_m\mathfrak{b}$, and by replacing any prime formula $\mathfrak{f}_i\mathfrak{a}_1 \ldots \mathfrak{a}_m = \mathfrak{f}_j\mathfrak{b}_1 \ldots \mathfrak{b}_n$ by $(E\mathfrak{c})(G_i\mathfrak{a}_1 \ldots \mathfrak{a}_m\mathfrak{c} \,\&\, G_j\mathfrak{b}_1 \ldots \mathfrak{b}_n\mathfrak{c})$. $\mathfrak{c}$ is an individual variable not occurring in $\mathfrak{C}(\mathfrak{f}_1, \ldots, \mathfrak{f}_k)$. Let $\mathfrak{E}(G_1, \ldots, G_k)$ be the disjunction of all wffs $(Ex_1) \ldots (Ex_m)(y)\overline{G_ix_1 \ldots x_my}$, where $m$ varies with $i$ and is the number of the arguments of $\mathfrak{f}_i$. Let $\mathfrak{G}(G_1, \ldots, G_k)$ may be the disjunction of all wffs

$$(Ex_1) \ldots (Ex_m)(Ey)(Ez)(G_ix_1 \ldots x_my \,\&\, G_ix_1 \ldots x_mz \,\&\, \overline{y=z}),$$

where $m$ is the same number as before. Lastly, let $\mathfrak{H}(G_1, \ldots, G_k)$ be the disjunction $\mathfrak{E}(G_1, \ldots, G_k) \vee \mathfrak{G}(G_1, \ldots, G_k) \vee \mathfrak{D}(G_1, \ldots, G_k)$. For any domain $\mathfrak{C}(\mathfrak{f}_1, \ldots, \mathfrak{f}_k)$ and $\mathfrak{H}(G_1, \ldots, G_k)$ are both valid or both not valid. The proofs, which present no difficulties, are omitted.

The foregoing remarks show that special solvable cases of the decision problem for the new wffs correspond to the special cases of the decision problem for the former wffs for which a solution has been given. In the following, we disregard these cases, nothing new appearing in them. Special cases of some generality of the decision problem for the wffs with functional variables are obtained by restriction to special classes of prefixes, or by limiting the number of the functional variables, etc. These cases do not correspond to the analogous cases for the wffs with predicate variables and cannot be solved by reference to them. We consider only wffs in prenex normal form without free individual variables.

I. *Solution for wffs having prefixes consisting solely of universal quantifiers*

The wff then has the form $(x_1) \dots (x_m)\mathfrak{A}(x_1, \dots, x_m)$. Let the functional variables occurring in it be $f_1, \dots, f_k$, $f_i$ being an $j_i$-adic variable. *The validity of such a wff is equivalent, for any domain, to that of an equality formula which we shall construct.*

In $\mathfrak{A}(x_1, \dots, x_m)$, let there occur $n$ distinct terms of the form $f_i\mathfrak{a}_1 \dots \mathfrak{a}_{j_i}$. Terms equally shaped are not counted twice. We replace each such term by one of the variables $y_1, \dots, y_n$, so that equally shaped terms, and only such, are replaced by the same variable. By this replacement, $\mathfrak{A}(x_1, \dots, x_m)$ goes over into a wff $\mathfrak{B}(x_1, \dots, x_m, y_1, \dots, y_n)$. Let $f_i\mathfrak{a}_1 \dots \mathfrak{a}_{j_i}$ and $f_i\mathfrak{b}_1 \dots \mathfrak{b}_{j_i}$ be two distinct terms of $\mathfrak{A}$, beginning with the same functional variable. To each such couple of terms we construct the wff $\mathfrak{a}_1 = \mathfrak{b}_1 \mathbin{\&} \mathfrak{a}_2 = \mathfrak{b}_2 \mathbin{\&} \dots \mathbin{\&} \mathfrak{a}_{j_i} = \mathfrak{b}_{j_i} \mathbin{\&} \overline{y_p = y_q}$, where $y_p$ and $y_q$ are the variables by which $f_i\mathfrak{a}_1 \dots \mathfrak{a}_{j_i}$ and $f_i\mathfrak{b}_1 \dots \mathfrak{b}_{j_i}$ have been replaced. Let $\mathfrak{K}_1, \dots, \mathfrak{K}_l$ be the wffs constructed in this way. Let $\mathfrak{C}(x_1, \dots, x_m, y_1, \dots, y_n)$ be the wff

$$\mathfrak{K}_1 \vee \mathfrak{K}_2 \vee \dots \vee \mathfrak{K}_l \vee \mathfrak{B}(x_1, \dots, x_m, y_1, \dots, y_n).$$

Our assertion is: $(x_1) \dots (x_m)\mathfrak{A}(x_1, \dots, x_m)$ and

$$(x_1) \dots (x_m)(y_1) \dots (y_n)\mathfrak{C}(x_1, \dots, x_m, y_1, \dots, y_n)$$

are valid in exactly the same domains.

If $(x_1) \dots (x_m)\mathfrak{A}(x_1, \dots, x_m)$ is not valid in a domain $D$, there is an assignment $\varphi_1, \dots, \varphi_k$ for $f_1, \dots, f_k$ and there are elements $a_1, \dots, a_m$ of $D$ such that $\mathfrak{A}(a_1, \dots, a_m)$ is false by $\varphi_1, \dots, \varphi_k$. Let the term of $\mathfrak{A}(x_1, \dots, x_m)$ which was replaced by $y_p$ before receive the value $b_p$ by the assignment $\varphi_1, \dots, \varphi_k, a_1, \dots, a_m$. By the assignment $a_1, \dots, a_m, b_1, \dots, b_n$ for $x_1, \dots, x_m, y_1, \dots, y_n$, obviously any of the wffs $\mathfrak{K}_1, \dots, \mathfrak{K}_l$ gets the value $F$, as does also $\mathfrak{B}(x_1, \dots, x_m, y_1, \dots, y_n)$ since the value of each term of the last wff is the same as that of the corresponding term in $\mathfrak{A}(x_1, \dots, x_m)$. Therefore,

$$(x_1) \dots (x_m)(y_1) \dots (y_n)\mathfrak{C}(x_1, \dots, x_m, y_1, \dots, y_n)$$

is not valid in $D$.

Let, on the other hand, $\mathfrak{C}(x_1, \dots, x_m, y_1, \dots, y_n)$ be false by an assignment $a_1, \dots, a_m, b_1, \dots, b_n$ in $D$. Functions $\varphi_1, \dots, \varphi_k$ over $D$ are defined thus: If the term $f_i\mathfrak{a}_1 \dots \mathfrak{a}_{j_i}$ of $\mathfrak{A}(x_1, \dots, x_m)$ has been previously replaced by $y_p$ and if $c_1, \dots, c_{j_i}$ are the values of $\mathfrak{a}_1, \dots, \mathfrak{a}_{j_i}$ by the assignment $a_1, \dots, a_m$ for $x_1, \dots, x_m$, then the value of $\varphi_i(c_1, \dots, c_{j_i})$ is $b_p$. Otherwise, the definition of the functions $\varphi_i$ is arbitrary. This definition is consistent, for the wffs $\mathfrak{K}_1, \dots, \mathfrak{K}_l$ are false by the assignment $a_1, \dots, a_m, b_1, \dots, b_n$. Because the valuation of the terms of $\mathfrak{A}(x_1, \dots, x_m)$ by the assignment $\varphi_1, \dots, \varphi_k, a_1, \dots, a_m$ is the same as that of the corresponding terms of $\mathfrak{B}(x_1, \dots, x_m, y_1, \dots, y_n)$ by the assignment $a_1, \dots, a_m$, $b_1, \dots, b_n$, $(x_1) \dots (x_m)$ $\mathfrak{A}(x_1, \dots, x_m)$ is false by the assignment $\varphi_1, \dots, \varphi_k$.

The translatability of the wffs with functional variables into wffs with predicate variables implies that each of the theorems of chapter V has its analogue here. The theorem concerning the Skolem normal form now takes a specially simple form, the proof of which may be sketched.

*Corresponding to every wff, one can construct another wff in prenex normal form with only existential quantifiers, so that both wffs are valid in exactly the same domains.*

We may assume the wff from which we start to be in prenex normal form and to begin with an existential quantifier. If it should begin with a universal quantifier, we add an existential quantifier at the beginning of the prefix, e.g. $(Ex)$, and subjoin the conjunction term $x=x$ to the matrix. $x$ is supposed not to occur in the wff in its original form. Let $(Ex_1) \dots (Ex_m)$ be the sequence of the first existential quantifiers and containing no universal quantifier. $(y)$ be the next quantifier; $\mathfrak{A}(x_1, \dots, x_n, y)$ the rest of the wff. We replace $(Ex_1) \dots (Ex_m)(y)\mathfrak{A}(x_1, \dots, x_m, y)$ by $(Ex_1) \dots (Ex_m)(Ey)(fx_1 \dots x_m = y \;\&\; \mathfrak{A}(x_1, \dots, x_m, y))$, where $f$ is a new functional variable. We restore the prenex normal form by placing the quantifiers of $\mathfrak{A}(x_1, \ldots, x_m, y)$ behind $(Ey)$ without changing their succession. By a finite repetition of this procedure, we get a wff with only existential quantifiers.

In the following, we shall therefore restrict ourselves to wffs in prenex normal form with only existential quantifiers. This property of the wffs is subsequently assumed without further comment.

## II. *Solution for wffs having only one monadic functional variable*

The wff has the form $(Ex_1) \ldots (Ex_m)\mathfrak{A}(x_1, \ldots, x_m)$. The only terms occurring in it are $x_1, \ldots, x_m, fx_1, \ldots, fx_m$. Instead of

$$(Ex_1) \ldots (Ex_m)\mathfrak{A}(x_1, \ldots, x_m),$$

we shall write $(Ex_1) \ldots (Ex_m)\mathfrak{A}(x_1, \ldots, x_m, fx_1, \ldots, fx_m)$. The decision problem shall be treated only in the form I.

*The wff is universally valid, if it is valid in the domains with* $1, 2, \ldots, m+1$ *elements.*

Let the wff be valid in the domains with $1, \ldots, m+1$ individuals. Further, let $D$ be a domain having more than $m+1$ elements and let $\varphi$ be a monadic function over this domain. We shall show that the wff is true in $D$ by $\varphi$.

We take an arbitrary element $a$ of $D$ and designate the elements $a, \varphi a, \varphi\varphi a, \ldots$ by $\varphi_0 a, \varphi_1 a, \varphi_2 a, \ldots$. We distinguish two cases.

1) There are no numbers $p$ and $q$ such that $p > q$, $\varphi_p a = \varphi_q a$ and $p - q \leqslant m+1$.

In this case, we find an element $b$ of the set $(\varphi_0 a, \varphi_1 a, \varphi_2 a, \ldots)$ such that the elements $b, \varphi_1 b, \ldots, \varphi_m b$ are different from each other. For instance $a$, as well as any element $\varphi_i a$, is an element with this property. According to our supposition $(Ex_1) \ldots (Ex_m)\ \mathfrak{A}(x_1, \ldots, x_m)$ is valid in a domain with $m+1$ elements. We shall show that this implies the validity in the domain $D$.

We now consider the domain $(b, \varphi_1 b, \ldots, \varphi_m b)$ which may by designated by $D_1$. In this domain, we define a function $\chi$ by $\chi\varphi_i b = \varphi_{i+1} b (1 \leqslant i+1 \leqslant m)$, $\chi\varphi_m b = b$. Let $\chi_0 c, \chi_1 c, \chi_2 c, \ldots$ again be abbreviations for $c, \chi c, \chi\chi c, \ldots$. According to our supposition, there are elements $c_1, \ldots, c_m$ in $D_1$ such that $\mathfrak{A}(c_1, \ldots, c_m, \chi c_1, \ldots, \chi c_m)$ is true. Since the domain $D_1$ consists of $m+1$ elements, it has an element, say $\chi_j b$, which is not identical with one of the elements $c_1, \ldots, c_m$. The definition of $\chi$ in $D_1$ makes it obvious that if $\mathfrak{A}(d_1, \ldots, d_m, \chi d_1, \ldots, \chi d_m)$ is true, then $\mathfrak{A}(\chi d_1, \ldots, \chi d_m, \chi\chi d_1, \ldots, \chi\chi d_m)$ is true for arbitrary $d_1, \ldots, d_m$, since for any elements $d_i$ and $d_k$, $d_i = d_k$ and $\chi d_i = \chi d_k$ are both true or both false. Therefore, $\mathfrak{A}(\chi_{m-j}c_1, \ldots, \chi_{m-j}c_m, \chi_{m+1-j}c_1, \ldots, \chi_{m+1-j}c_m)$ is true. None of the elements $\chi_{m-j}c_1, \ldots, \chi_{m-j}c_m$ is identical with $\chi_m b$, since $c_1, \ldots, c_m$ were not identical with $\chi_j b$. We thus have found elements $e_1, \ldots, e_m$ such that $\mathfrak{A}(e_1, \ldots, e_m, \chi e_1, \ldots, \chi e_m)$ is true, every $e_i$ being different from $\chi_m b$. Since the function $\chi$ in $D_1$ and the function $\varphi$ in $D$ do not differ as regards the elements $e_1, \ldots, e_m$, $\mathfrak{A}(e_1, \ldots, e_m, \varphi e_1, \ldots, \varphi e_m)$ is true in $D$. This means that $(Ex_1) \ldots (Ex_m)\mathfrak{A}(x_1, \ldots, x_m, \varphi x_1, \ldots, \varphi x_m)$ is true in $D$.

2) There are numbers $p$ and $q$ such that $p > q$, $\varphi_p a = \varphi_q a$, and $p - q \leqslant m + 1$.

Let $p$ and $q$ be such a pair. We consider the domain $D_2$ consisting of the elements $\varphi_q a, \varphi_{q+1} a, \ldots, \varphi_{p-1} a$. We define a function $\chi$ in $D_2$ by $\chi\varphi_i a = \varphi_{i+1} a$, $(q + 1 \leqslant i + 1 \leqslant p - 1)$, and $\chi\varphi_{p-1} a = \varphi_q a$. The function $\chi$ for this domain is the same as $\varphi$ in $D$ as far as elements of $D_2$ are concerned. According to our supposition,

$$(Ex_1) \ldots (Ex_m)\mathfrak{A}(x_1, \ldots, x_m, \chi x_1, \ldots, \chi x_m)$$

is true in $D_2$; this immediately implies that

$$(Ex_1) \ldots (Ex_m)\mathfrak{A}(x_1, \ldots, x_m, \varphi x_1, \ldots, \varphi x_m)$$

is true in $D$.

Since $\varphi$ was arbitrary, our wff is valid in $D$.

### III. *Solution for wffs having prefixes containing only one existential quantifier*

If $(Ex)$ is the quantifier, the terms of the wff different from $x$ have a form $fx$, $gxx$, $hxxx$, and so forth. It is easy to see that in this wff the $n$-adic functions $(n \geqslant 2)$ can be replaced by monadic functions in writing $g_1x$, $h_1x$, ... for $gxx$, $hxxx$, .... We may therefore assume the wff to have a form $(Ex)\mathfrak{A}(x, f_1x, \ldots, f_nx)$.

$$(f_1) \dots (f_n)(Ex)\mathfrak{A}(x, f_1x, \dots, f_nx)$$

is equivalent to

$$(Ex)(y_1) \dots (y_n)\mathfrak{A}(x, y_1, \dots, y_n).$$

*The decision problem for this case therefore reduces to that for equality formulas.*

This solution is obtained by a repeated application of a general *elimination theorem* corresponding to the elimination theorems $E23$—$E25$ of IV, § 2. The theorem, or better the theorems, run as follow.

$E27$. Let $f$ be a monadic functional variable occurring in a wff $\mathfrak{A}(x, fx)$ only in the form $fx$. $\mathfrak{A}(x, fx)$ may contain quantifiers (functional and individual ones) and free variables. $(f)(Ex)\mathfrak{A}(x, fx)$ is then equivalent to $(Ex)(y)\mathfrak{A}(x, y)$, where $y$ is a new variable. Likewise, let $\mathfrak{B}$ be a wff in which the dyadic functional variable $g$ occurs only in a form $gx\mathfrak{a}$, $\mathfrak{a}$ being possibly different in the different places. To express this we write $\mathfrak{B}$ in the form $\mathfrak{B}_y(x, gxy)$. Let $\mathfrak{C}$ result from $\mathfrak{B}$ by replacing every term $gx\mathfrak{a}$ by $h\mathfrak{a}$, where $h$ is a new monadic functional variable. $\mathfrak{C}$ can be written in the form $\mathfrak{B}_y(x, hy)$. $(g)(Ex)\mathfrak{B}_y(x, gxy)$ is then equivalent to $(Ex)(h)\mathfrak{B}_y(x, hy)$.

If $(Ex)(y)\mathfrak{A}(x, y)$ is false in $D$ by an assignment $\Omega$ for its free variables, there is an element $b$ for every element $a$ of $D$ such that $\mathfrak{A}(a, b)$ is false by $\Omega$. For every $a$ we can select a $b$ such that a monadic function $\varphi$ is defined over $D$ and such that $\mathfrak{A}(a, \varphi a)$ is false by $\Omega$ for every $a$; then $(f)(Ex)\mathfrak{A}(x, fx)$ cannot be true by $\Omega$. If $(f)(Ex)\mathfrak{A}(x, fx)$ is false by an assignment $\Omega$, there is a function $\varphi$ over $D$ such that for every $a$ of $D$, $\overline{\mathfrak{A}(a, \varphi a)}$ and therefore $(x)(Ey)\overline{\mathfrak{A}(x, y)}$, is true by $\Omega$. This excludes the truth of $(Ex)(y)\mathfrak{A}(x, y)$ by $\Omega$.

If $(g)(Ex)\mathfrak{B}_y(x, gxy)$ is false in $D$ by an assignment $\Omega$, there is a dyadic function $\psi$ such that $\mathfrak{B}_y(a, \psi ay)$ is false for every $a$ by $\Omega$. Then to every $a$ there exists a monadic function $\chi$ defined by $(y)(\chi y = \psi ay)$ such that $\mathfrak{B}_y(a, \chi y)$ is false by $\Omega$. $(Ex)(h)\mathfrak{B}_p(x, hy)$ is then false by $\Omega$. If $(Ex)(h)\mathfrak{B}_y(x, hy)$ is false by $\Omega$, there is a function $\chi$ for every $a$ of $D$ such that $\mathfrak{B}_y(a, \chi y)$ is false by $\Omega$. For every $a$ we select such a function and call it $\chi_a$. $\chi_a$ defines a duadic function $\varphi$

for which for all $a$ and $b$, $\varphi ab = \chi_a b$. Since $\mathfrak{B}_v(a, \varphi ay)$ is always false by $\Omega$, so is $(g)(Ex)\mathfrak{B}_v(x, gxy)$.

In general, special cases of the decision problem for the wffs with functional variables are of course not easier to solve than the corresponding cases for the wffs with predicate variables; but they offer a different trend of investigation.

The decision problem can also be formulated for wffs which contain both functional and predicate variables; it may be advantageous sometimes to pass to such wffs. Definition and valuation of such wffs are easily given.

## BIBLIOGRAPHY

Besides the papers on solvable cases of the decision problem and some other works cited from the text, this list contains the papers on the reduction theory of the decision problem and those original papers in which the impossibility of a general solution of the decision problem was first shown. The numerous works concerning undecidability in special mathematical systems are not included.


Ackermann, Wilhelm (see also Hilbert and Ackermann):

1. Über die Erfüllbarkeit gewisser Zählausdrücke. Mathematische Annalen **100** (1928), pp. 638–649.
2. Untersuchungen über das Eliminationsproblem der mathematischen Logik. Math. Annalen **110** (1934), pp. 390–413.
3. Zum Eliminationsproblem der mathematischen Logik. Math. Annalen **111** (1935), pp. 61–63.
4. Beiträge zum Entscheidungsproblem der mathematischen Logik. Math. Annalen **112** (1936), pp. 419–432.

Behmann, Heinrich:

1. Beiträge zur Algebra der Logik, insbesondere zum Entscheidungsproblem. Math. Annalen **86** (1922), pp. 163–229.
2. Algebra der Logik und Entscheidungsproblem. Jahresbericht DMV **32** (1923), 2. Abt., pp. 66–67.
3. Entscheidungsproblem und Logik der Beziehungen. Jahresbericht DMV **36** (1927), 2. Abt., pp. 17–18.

Bernays, Paul und Schönfinkel, Moses (see also Hilbert and Bernays):

1. Zum Entscheidungsproblem der mathematischen Logik. Math. Annalen **99** (1928), pp. 401–419.

Church, Alonzo:

1. An unsolvable theorem of elementary number theory. Amer. Journ. of Math. **58** (1936), pp. 345–363.
2. A note on the Entscheidungsproblem. Journ. of Symbol. Logic **1** (1936), pp. 40–41; Correction ibid., pp. 101–102.
3. Special cases of the decision problem. Revue philos. de Louvain **49** (1951), pp. 203–221. A correction, ibid. **50** (1952), pp. 270–272.

Church, Alonzo and Quine, Willard van Orman:

1. Some theorems on definability and decidability. Journ. of Symbol. Logic **17** (1952), pp. 179–187.

GÉGALKINE, I.:

1. Sur l'Entscheidungsproblem. Russian with French abstract. Recueil mathématique, Moscou **6** (1939), pp. 185–198.
2. Sur le problème de la résolubilité pour les classes finies. Russian with French abstract. Moskovski Gosudarstvenni Universitet, Udenye zapiski, **100** (1946), pp. 155–211.

GENTZEN, GERHARD:

1. Untersuchungen über das logische Schließen; I, II. Math. Zeitschrift **39** (1934), pp. 176–210, pp. 405–431.

GÖDEL, KURT:

1. Die Vollständigkeit der Axiome des logischen Funktionenkalküls. Monatsh. für Math. u. Physik **37** (1930), pp. 349–360.
2. Ein Spezialfall des Entscheidungsproblems der theoretischen Logik. Ergebn. math. Kolloquium **2** (1932).
3. Zum Entscheidungsproblem des logischen Funktionenkalküls. Monatsh. Math. Phys. **40** (1933), pp. 433–443.

HILBERT, DAVID und BERNAYS, PAUL:

1. Grundlagen der Mathematik. Vol. I, (1934) (§ 4, d, e,; § 5). Vol. II (1939), (§ 3, 5).

HILBERT, DAVID und ACKERMANN, WILHELM:

1. Grundzüge der theoretischen Logik. 3rd ed. 1949 (Springer) (II, § 2; III, §§ 11, 12).

HERBRAND, JACQUES:

1. Recherches sur la théorie de la demonstration. Traveaux de la Société des Sciences et des Lettres de Varsovie, Cl. III math.-phys., **33** (1930), 128 pp.
2. Sur le problème fondamental de la Logique Mathématique. Comptes Rendus des Séances de la Société des Sciences et des Lettres de Varsovie, Cl. III, **24** (1931).

KALMÁR, LÁSZLÓ:

1. Eine Bemerkung zur Entscheidungstheorie. Acta litt. ac sci. Reg. Univers. Hung. Franc. Joseph., Sectio sci. math. **4** (1928/29), pp. 248–252.
2. Ein Beitrag zum Entscheidungsproblem. Ibid. **5** (1930/32), pp. 222–236.
3. Zum Entscheidungsproblem der mathematischen Logik. Verhandl. Internat. Math. Kongr. Zürich 1932 (2), pp. 337–338.
4. Über die Erfüllbarkeit derjenigen Zählausdrücke, welche in der Nor-

malform zwei benachbarte Allzeichen enthalten. Math. Annalen **108** (1933), pp. 466–484.
5. Über einen Löwenheimschen Satz. Acta litt. ac scient., math. **7** (1934/35), pp. 112–121.
6. Zurückführung des Entscheidungsproblems auf den Fall von Formeln mit einer einzigen binären Funktionsvariablen. Compositio Mathematica **4** (1936), pp. 137–144.
7. Zur Reduktionstheorie des Entscheidungsproblems. Norsk Matematisk Tidsskrift **19** (1937), pp. 121–130.
8. On the reduction of the decision problem. First paper. Ackermann prefix, a single binary predicate. Journ. of Symbol. Logic **4** (1939), pp. 1–9.
9. Contributions to the reduction theory of the decision problem. English with Russian abstract. Acta math. Acad. Sci. Hung. I, **73** (1950), pp. 64–73.
10. Contributions to the reduction theory of the decision problem, fourth paper. Acta Math. Acad. Sci. Hung. II, 1951, pp. 125–142.

KALMÁR, LÁSZLÓ and SURÁNYI, JÁNOS:

1. On the reduction of the decision problem. Second paper. Gödel prefix, a single binary predicate. Journ. of Symb. Logic **12** (1947), pp. 65–73.
2. On the decision problem. Third paper. Pepis prefix, a single binary predicate. ibid. **15** (1950), pp. 161–173.

LANGFORD, COOPER HAROLD:

1. Some theorems on deducibility. Annals of Mathematics. **28** (1926/27), pp. 16–40.
2. Theorems on deducibility (Second paper), ibid., pp. 459–471.

LÖWENHEIM, LEOPOLD:

1. Über Möglichkeiten im Relativkalkül. Math. Annalen **76** (1915), pp. 137–148.

MCKINSEY, J. C. C.:

1. The decision problem for some classes of sentences without quantifiers. Journ. of Symb. Logic **8** (1943), pp. 61–76.

PEPIS, JOZEF:

1. Beiträge zur Reduktionstheorie des logischen Entscheidungsproblems. Acta Sci. Math. Szeged **8** (1936), pp. 7–41.
2. Untersuchungen über das Entscheidungsproblem der mathematischen Logik. Fund. Math. **30** (1938), pp. 257–338.
3. Eine Verfahren der mathematischen Logik. Journ. of Symb. Logic **3** (1938), pp. 61–76.

Post, Emil L.:

1. Formal reductions of the general combinatorial decision problem. Amer. Journ. of Math. **65** (1943), pp. 197–215.

Presburger, M.:

1. Über die Vollständigkeit eines gewissen Systems der Arithmetik ganzer Zahlen, in welchem die Addition als einzige Operation hervortritt. Comptes Rendus du I. Congrès des Mathématiciens des Pays Slaves. Warsaw 1930, pp. 92–101.

Quine, Willard van Orman (see also Church and Quine):

1. On the Logic of Quantification. Journ. Symbol. Logic **10** (1945), pp. 1–12.

Schütte, Kurt:

1. Untersuchungen zum Entscheidungsproblem der mathematischen Logik. Math. Annalen **109** (1934), pp. 572–603.
2. Über die Erfüllbarkeit einer Klasse von logischen Formeln. ibid. **110** (1934), pp. 161–194.
3. Schlußweisen-Kalküle der Prädikatenlogik. ibid. **122** (1950) pp. 47–65.

Skolem, Thoralf:

1. Untersuchungen über die Axiome des Klassenkalküls and über Produktations- und Summationsprobleme, welche gewisse Klassen von Aussagen betreffen. Skrifter utgit av Vidensk. i Kristiania, I, Math.-nat. Klasse 1919, no. **3**, 37 pp.
2. Logisch-kombinatorische Untersuchungen über die Erfüllbarkeit oder Beweisbarkeit mathematischer Sätze nebst einem Theorem über dichte Mengen. Ibid. 1920, no. **4**, 36 pp.
3. Über die mathematische Logik. Norsk Mat. Tidsskrift **106** (1928), pp. 125–142.
4. Über einige Satzfunktionen in der Arithmetik. Skrifter Norsk Vid. Akademi Oslo, I mat.-nat. Klasse, no. **7** (1931), 28 pp.
5. Ein kombinatorischer Satz mit Anwendung auf ein logisches Entscheidungsproblem. Fund. Math. **20** (1933), pp. 254–261.
6. Über die Erfüllbarkeit gewisser Zählausdrücke. Skrifter Norsk Vid. Akademi Oslo, I, Mat.-nat. Klasse, no. **6** (1935), 14 pp.
7. Über die Erfüllbarkeit von einigen Zählausdrücken. Vid. Skrifter, Oslo, no. **8** (1935).
8. Ein Satz über Zählausdrücke, Acta Sci. Math. Szeged **7** (1934/35), pp. 193–199.
9. Einige Reduktionen des Entscheidungsproblems. Avh. Vid. Akad. Oslo I, Mat.-nat. Klasse no. **6** (1936), 17 pp.

SURÁNYI, JÁNOS (see also Kalmar and Surányi):

1. Zur Reduktion des Entscheidungsproblems des logischen Funktionenkalküls. Mat. es Fizikai Lapok **50** (1943), pp. 51–74.
2. Reduction of the decision problem to formulas containing a bounded number of quantifiers only. Proc. Xth Int. Congr. Philos., Amsterdam, I, (1949), pp. 759–762.
3. Contributions to the reduction theory of the decision problem, fifth paper. Acta Math. Acad. Sci. Hung. II 1951, pp. 325ff.

TARSKI, ALFRED:

1. Der Wahrheitsbegriff in den formalisierten Sprachen. Studi aphilosophica, Lemberg **1** (1936), pp. 261–405.
2. Actual. sci. industr. **394**, pp. 1–11, Paris 1936.
3. A decision method for elementary algebra and geometry. The Rand Corporation, Santa Monica, California, (1948), 60 pp.

TURING, ALAN MATHISON:

1. On computable numbers, with an application to the Entscheidungsproblem. Proc. London Math. Soc. **42** (1936/37), pp. 230–265. A correction, ibid. **43** (1937), pp. 544–546.

TRACHTENBROD, B. A.:

1. (Impossibility of an algorithm for the decision problem in finite classes). Russian. Doklady Akademii Nauk SSSR, n.s., **70** (1950), pp. 569–572.

VON WRIGHT, G. H.:

1. On the idea of logical truth (I). Soc. Sci. Fennica. Comment. phys.-math., vol. **14**, no. 4, 1948, 20 pp.
2. On the idea of logical truth (II), ibid., vol. **15**, no. 10, 1950, 45 pp.
3. On double quantification. Ibid. vol. **16**, no. 3, 1952, 14 pp.

SMIELEW, W.:

1. Decision problem in group theory. Proc. Xth Int. Congr. Philos., Amsterdam 1948, vol. I, pp. 373–376.

# INDEX